NATURAL ENVIRONMENT

INSTITUTE OF GEOL(

Geological Survey

BRITISH REGIONAL GEOLOGY

BRISTOL AND GLOUCESTER DISTRICT

By

F. B. A. WELCH, B.Sc., Ph.D.

and R. CROOKALL, D.Sc., Ph.D.

SECOND EDITION

by

G. A. KELLAWAY, B.Sc.

and F. B. A. WELCH, B.Sc., Ph.D.

LONDON

HER MAJESTY'S STATIONERY OFFICE

1948

CONTENTS

ILLUSTRATIONS

FIGURES IN TEXT

PLATES

(A 6037)

CHEDDAR GORGE

BRISTOL AND GLOUCESTER DISTRICT

I. INTRODUCTION

AREA AND PHYSIOGRAPHY

THE 'BRISTOL AND GLOUCESTER DISTRICT' comprises the Cotswolds and the Severn Estuary region, and includes the greater part of the counties of Gloucestershire and Somerset (excluding West Somerset); also, for geological continuity, small parts of the counties of Monmouthshire, Herefordshire and Worcestershire.

Geologically speaking, it is one of the most varied districts of Britain, for, with the exception of the Ordovician and possibly the Permian, there is exposed at the surface every geological formation from the Cambrian to the Cretaceous.

The geological map (Fig. 1) shows that the central part of the region is occupied by a triangular area of Palaeozoic rocks (concealed in many places by a thin

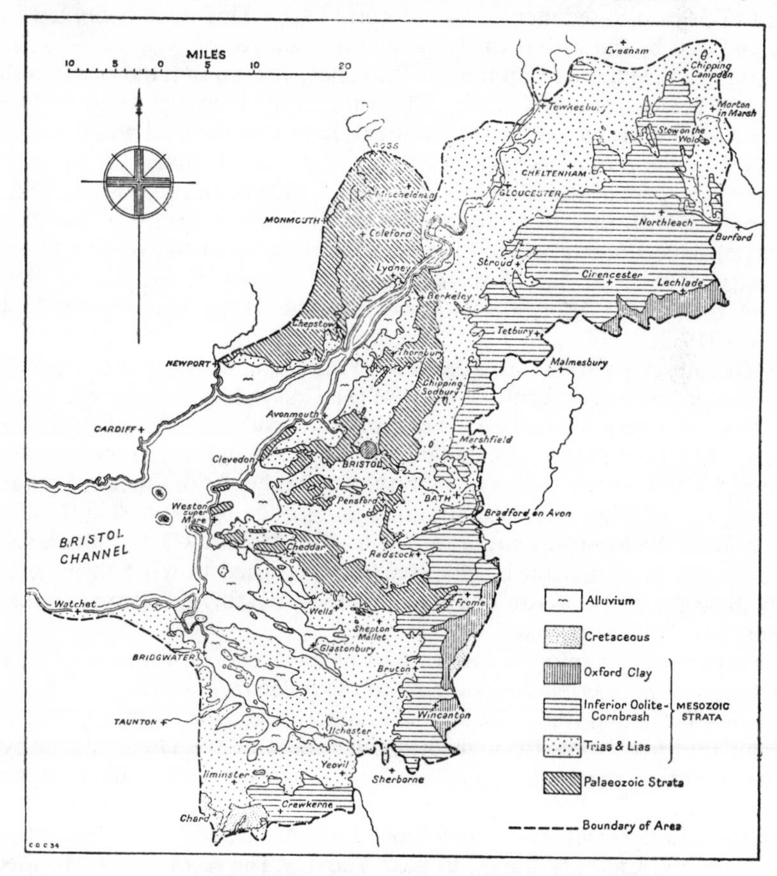

FIG. 1. *Sketch-map of the geology of the district*

covering of Mesozoic strata) extending from the Forest of Dean to the Mendips. To the south and north-east of this Palaeozoic triangle lie unbroken stretches of Mesozoic sediments.

The distribution of high and low ground is related both to the nature of the underlying rocks, and to the denudation to which they have been subjected. In general the Palaeozoic rocks, by reason of their relative hardness, give rise to areas of moderately high relief. In parts of south Gloucestershire and north Somerset, however, the outcrops of the Cambrian, Silurian, Old Red Sandstone and Carboniferous beds are characterized by low undulating country. This apparent anomaly is due to the fact that the sculpturing of the modern landscape has stripped off the Mesozoic covering from these older strata, revealing a part of an ancient erosion-surface which had been reduced to very low relief before it was covered by sediments in Mesozoic times.

In the west of the district Palaeozoic rocks give rise to the relatively high ground of the Forest of Dean and Chepstow area, bordering the broad valley of the Severn carved mainly out of soft Mesozoic sediments.

To the south-west and south of Bristol, Palaeozoic rocks form areas of moderate relief lying between 500 and 600 ft. above sea-level. These comprise the Long Ashton to Clevedon ridge which is separated by the Flax Bourton valleys from the high, dome-like mass of Broadfield Down with Dundry Hill, formed of Mesozoic sediments, on the north-east. This mass is limited to the south and east by the valleys of the Yeo and Chew rivers.

Apart from the inlier of Cannington Park, near Bridgwater, the most southerly outcrop of Palaeozoic rocks in the district forms the long high ridge of Mendip which runs from Frome on the east to Brean Down on the west and is continued out to sea by the rocky islands of Flatholm and Steep Holme. At three points in the western part of the Mendips a height of 1000 ft. or more is reached.

In contrast with this, there lies to the south of the Mendips a vast expanse of alluvial flats concealing extensive depressions scoured out of soft Mesozoic sediments. The dead flat of these moors or ' levels ' is broken by the low ridge of the Polden Hills, Brent Knoll and the gently rising ground above Wedmore (Pl. XI).

Running roughly parallel with the eastern margin of the district comparatively hard Jurassic limestones form the mass of the Cotswolds, whose great indented, wall-like scarp, overlooking the Vale of the Severn, runs from Chipping Campden to Bath. At Cleeve Hill, near Cheltenham, the Cotswolds reach their maximum height of 1,070 ft. Southwards to Bath the general height of the range gradually decreases, the hills around Bath attaining an altitude of 600 to 750 ft. To the south of Bath the Mesozoic strata form a tract of ground which, though seldom exceeding 600 ft. in general height, is strikingly varied in relief through being deeply dissected by the Avon and its tributaries, notably the River Frome and the Cam and Wellow brooks.

This region merges into the eastern part of the Mendips, where the Mesozoic rocks form a thin intermittent covering to the Palaeozoic strata.

Between Bath and the Mendips the outcrop of the Jurassic limestones separates into two bands through the replacement of the Great Oolite by the clay formation of the Fuller's Earth. Two roughly parallel ridges, separated from one another by low ground, are thus formed. The Inferior Oolite gives rise to the range of hills that runs from Lamyatt Beacon, near Bruton, past Castle Cary and Cadbury Camp, to near Yeovil. The second ridge, formed by the Forest Marble, lies to the east and extends from Wanstrow, past Redlynch, to Bratton. South of this point it comprises the eminences of Charlton Hill and East Hill near Milborne Port and, outside the district, the ridge of Holt and Lillington Hills lying to the south-east of Sherborne. Between Yeovil and Crewkerne the Forest Marble limestones form the Abbott's Hill and Ashlands Hill ridge which in places reaches a height of nearly 600 ft.

The drainage of the district is comparatively simple: practically all rivers west of the Cotswold scarp flow into the Severn Estuary, whilst those which follow the dip-slope of the Cotswolds join the Thames (*see* Fig. 2). The Bristol Avon is an exception. Rising within the eastern margin of the district at

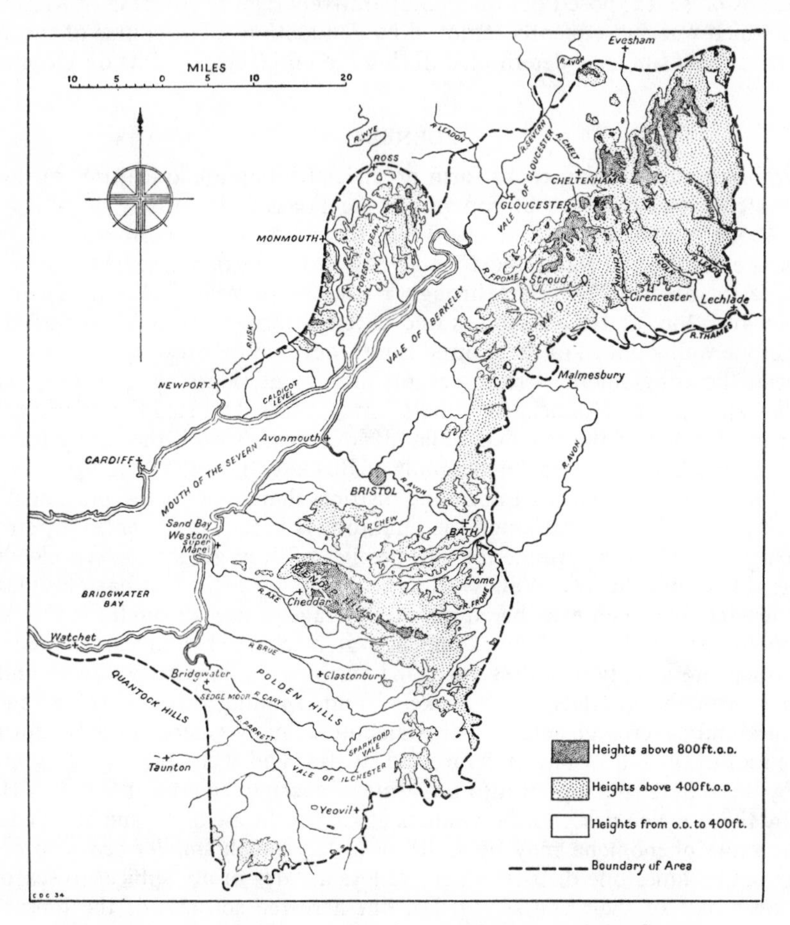

FIG. 2. *Sketch-map of the physical features of the district*

Badminton, it flows eastwards as a consequent stream down the dip-slope of the Cotswolds for about ten miles to Malmesbury, as if belonging to the Thames drainage system. At Malmesbury it turns south-west and follows the strike of the Jurassic beds to Bradford-on-Avon, whence it flows west and north to Bath, re-entering the district at Limpley Stoke. In its passage to Bath it runs against the dip of the Jurassic rocks and cuts a wide, deep valley (Pl. IX). From Bath to Hanham Mills the river flows mainly over Keuper and Liassic strata and then cuts a gorge in Coal Measures sandstone from which it emerges at

Bristol. Here it turns as if heading for the Low Flax Bourton Valley and the sea at Clevedon, but instead of following this apparently easy route along the outcrop of the soft Triassic rocks it turns north-west at Clifton and enters the famous gorge carved in hard Carboniferous grits and limestones (Pl. IV). Before flowing into the Severn Estuary at Avonmouth it is joined at Sea Mills by the Trym, which cuts a similar, though smaller, gorge through the Carboniferous Limestone ridge near Henbury.

The Avon and its tributaries thus appear to represent superimposed drainage; i.e. their present anomalous courses were initiated not on the rocks and land surface at present exposed but on a comparatively regular covering of Mesozoic rocks which was subsequently removed by denudation. The course of the Wye may have been similarly determined during the initial stages of its development.

SCENERY

Cambrian and Silurian rocks form no special topographic features owing to the limited extent of their outcrop and to the Triassic planation.

In Monmouthshire, west of the Wye, the massive Brownstones and conglomerates of the Old Red Sandstone give rise to fine wooded scarps that sweep north-eastwards from Newport through Wentwood to near Trellech. Their soil is poor and thin, and the region is one of small farms with fields bounded by thick stone walls: much of the ground is now devoted to forestry. In the Forest of Dean the conglomerates form several prominent ridges such as Edge Hill, Soudley and Coppet Hill near Symond's Yat (Pl. III). Old Red Sandstone rocks give rise to much of the wooded Failand ridge near Bristol, the sandy tract of Milbury Heath and the desolate summit of Blackdown in the Mendips.

It is in the Carboniferous Limestone districts that some of the most striking scenery is to be found. Although the limestone is hard it is traversed by strong vertical joints which determine the cliff profiles of deep gorges such as Cheddar Gorge (Pl. I) and the Wye Valley (Pl. V). These are incised in barren uplands like the Mendips where weathered limestone crags project through the thin soil. Owing to the solubility of limestone in waters charged with carbon dioxide such tracts are usually waterless: streams reaching the limestone plunge underground through 'swallets' or 'slockers' and, running through subterranean passages and caverns glistening with stalactites, finally emerge in great springs at the foot of the hills. The underground streams and their springs are exemplified by the waters which pour into Eastwater Cavern to emerge at Wookey Hole and by those which descend the swallets at Charterhouse and issue at Cheddar.

The same phenomena may be seen, on a very much smaller scale, in some of the oolitic limestone districts where valleys are dry or are subject to seasonal flow over part of their course (Pl. II), but here the softness of the limestone precludes the formation of deep gorges.

The scenery of the Coal Measures often contrasts strongly with that of the Carboniferous Limestone. Consisting mainly of shales with a thick median division of sandstone known as Pennant Grit, they give rise, in the Forest of Dean, to thickly-wooded undulating ground of moderate relief in which the sandstones form ridges. The scenery of the Bristol Coalfield is monotonous and shows little of that differentiation of relief that might have been expected from the occurrence of alternating hard and soft rocks—a phenomenon due to the late Triassic planation. In the Somerset Coalfields, however, this pre-Triassic surface has been uncovered in a few places only, and over the remainder of the

(A 4240)

A.—Dry Valley Floored by Permeable Limestone

(A 4243)

B.—Permanent Stream on Impermeable Clay Floor

THE DIKLER VALLEY, NORTH COTSWOLDS

(A 6262)

THE WYE VALLEY, LOOKING NORTHWARDS FROM SYMOND'S YAT TO THE OLD RED SANDSTONE RIDGE OF COPPET HILL

area the Coal Measures are concealed by Mesozoic strata which impress their individuality upon the scenery.

The predominantly soft nature of the Trias and Lias gives rise to areas of low relief such as the vales of Gloucester and Somerset. The scenery is not, however, without charm: the level country through which the Severn flows forms miles of rich pasture and orchards, broken occasionally by undulating ridges of harder rock which at Tewkesbury, Westbury and Fretherne make low cliffs.

In Somerset the Blue Lias limestones form the Poldens and other low ranges of hills separating the fertile plains of red Triassic marl from the heavy clay lands of the Lower Lias.

Southwards from Stroud the Upper Lias Sands crop out in the face of the Cotswold escarpment, and in south and east Somerset give rise to steep sandy slopes and knolls such as those of Glastonbury Tor and Montacute. Deeply sunken lanes or ' holloways ' are a characteristic feature of this type of country.

The chief natural feature of the region is the great mural scarp of the Cotswolds, extending from Chipping Campden to Bath, formed by the Inferior and Great Oolite limestones. The former, dominating the escarpment in the North and Mid Cotswolds, is gradually replaced in importance in the South Cotswolds by the Great Oolite of the uplands overlooking the Avon Valley at Bath.

On the dip-slopes, the limestones, falling gently eastward towards the Oxford Clay vales, give rise to a high undulating plateau, partly arable, partly downland, drained by the head-waters of the Thames and Avon, and providing shelter in its deep valleys for villages and mansions built of mellow freestone.

South of the Mendips no great single escarpment is present. Its place is taken by two step-like ridges; the lower and more westerly, formed by the Inferior Oolite, is separated from the higher scarp of the Forest Marble by a tract of Fuller's Earth Clay in which the Fuller's Earth Rock makes a minor feature. East of the Forest Marble ridge lies a wide expanse of the heavy Oxford Clay, bordered on its eastern margin by the escarpments of the Greensand and Chalk.

A widely differing type of scenery, covering some 200 to 300 square miles, is that produced by the alluvium of the Somerset Levels. Various parts of the area are known as Moors or Heaths, as for example Sedgemoor and Meare Heath. Much of the ground is below high-tide level and is protected from marine inundation by dunes of blown sand and sea-walls. The rivers Axe, Brue, Parret and Cary (the last being continued seaward as the artificial King's Sedgemoor Drain) flow sluggishly westwards through a vast region of fields bounded by willow-lined ditches or ' rhines '. The flat landscape throws into relief the great southern face of the Mendips (Pl. X), the inliers of Mesozoic rocks which form the Poldens and the striking residual hills of Glastonbury Tor and Brent Knoll.

EARLY GEOLOGICAL WORK

Of all the names connected with the geology of the district none is greater than that of William Smith, the ' Father of English Geology '. Whilst engaged in surveying the Somerset Coal Canal in 1792–5 he came to discover the fundamental principles of stratigraphy—the constancy of the order of succession of the strata and the characterization of each stratum by certain fossil species. In 1799 he coloured geologically the ' Map of Five Miles around the City of Bath ', one of the oldest geological maps in existence. At Bath in June of the same year, he dictated his ' Tabular View of the Order of Strata ' to his friends Townsend and Richardson.

The official 1 inch to 1 mile Geological Survey maps of the Bristol-Gloucester District all appeared between 1845 and 1857 and were the results of the labours of such well-known men as Sir H. T. De la Beche, John Phillips, A. C. Ramsay, H. W. Bristow, W. T. Aveline, D. H. Williams and Edward Hull.

Mention must also be made of the remarkable set of 19 sheets of maps of the Bristol Coalfields, on the scale of 4 inches to 1 mile, produced in 1862 by William Sanders. These maps formed the basis of the local work of the 1871 Coal Commission in which John Anstie played a great part.

In addition to the official maps and publications there are descriptions of the geology of the district by many private workers. The name of Weaver will be remembered for his observations in 1824 on the Silurian rocks of Tortworth, and that of Charles Moore for his labours on the Rhaetic and Liassic rocks.

Much of our present knowledge of the Somerset Coalfield is due to the detailed work of James McMurtrie, whilst in literature on the Carboniferous Limestone the name of Arthur Vaughan stands pre-eminent. The lucid and stimulating papers of Charles Lloyd Morgan did much to inspire research into the geological history and structure of the Bristol district and had the effect of arousing great popular interest in the science.

Many well-known names figure in works upon the Oolites: Wright, Lycett, Hudleston, Witchell to mention a few, but the most famous is that of S. S. Buckman, whose work is referred to later.

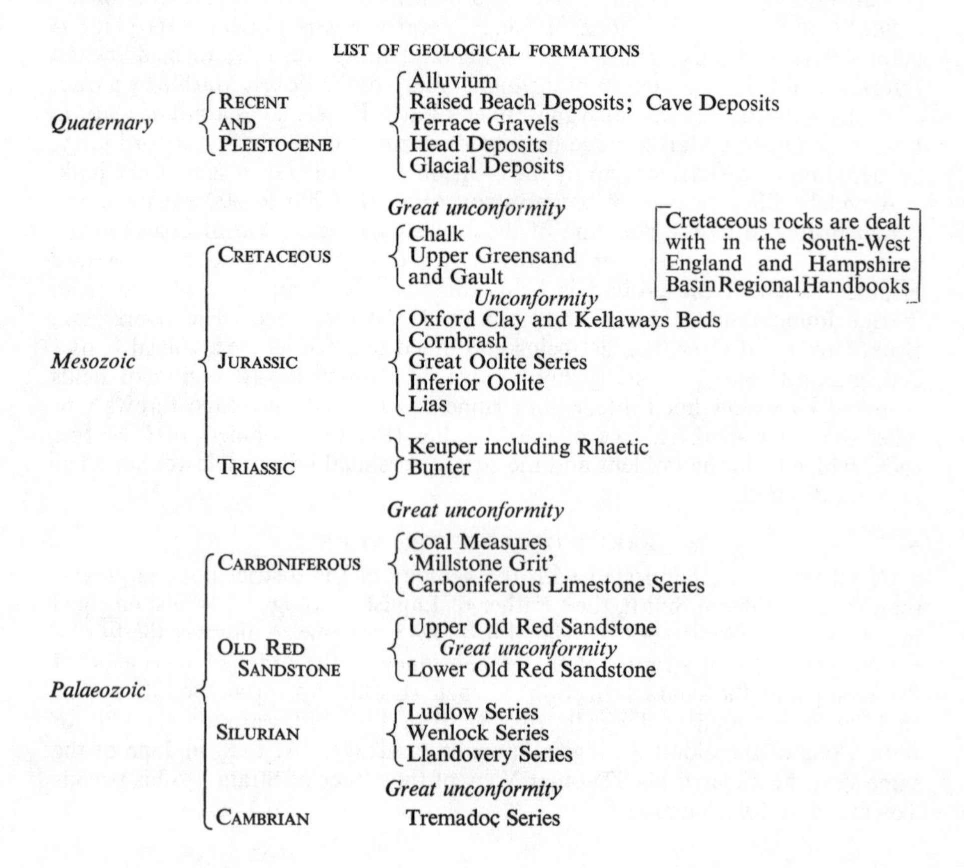

LIST OF GEOLOGICAL FORMATIONS

Era	System	Formations
Quaternary	RECENT AND PLEISTOCENE	Alluvium Raised Beach Deposits; Cave Deposits Terrace Gravels Head Deposits Glacial Deposits
		Great unconformity
Mesozoic	CRETACEOUS	Chalk Upper Greensand and Gault [Cretaceous rocks are dealt with in the South-West England and Hampshire Basin Regional Handbooks]
		Unconformity
	JURASSIC	Oxford Clay and Kellaways Beds Cornbrash Great Oolite Series Inferior Oolite Lias
	TRIASSIC	Keuper including Rhaetic Bunter
		Great unconformity
Palaeozoic	CARBONIFEROUS	Coal Measures 'Millstone Grit' Carboniferous Limestone Series
	OLD RED SANDSTONE	Upper Old Red Sandstone *Great unconformity* Lower Old Red Sandstone
	SILURIAN	Ludlow Series Wenlock Series Llandovery Series
		Great unconformity
	CAMBRIAN	Tremadoç Series

II. STRUCTURAL AND DEPOSITIONAL HISTORY

A GLANCE at the geological map of the region will show that in the Palaeozoic rocks two main sets of fold lines can be distinguished, the one running approximately N-S or NE-SW; and the other E-W. The former is typified by the main syncline of the Bristol Coalfield, the latter by the Mendip chain. To the N-S fold lines the name ' Malvernoid ' is applied, to the NE-SW ' Caledonoid ', whilst those of a dominantly E-W trend are termed ' Armoricanoid '.

Two major Caledonoid fold lines, called the Lower Severn and Bath axes (Fig. 3), produce a fold-pattern shaped like a slightly bent tuning-fork, since the two axes converge in the northern part of the area and, after uniting, continue northwards with a Malvernoid trend. The Caledonoid and Malvernoid axes, which have a longer history than those with an E-W trend, plunge beneath the younger folds of the Mendip Axis.

The significance of these axes lies in the fact that they perpetuate lines of structural weakness and that throughout geological history deep-seated earth-movements have taken place along them. Even during relatively quiescent periods there was a tendency for uplift to take place along these belts of instability so that the sea-floor was subject to local elevation leading to the development of a shallow water facies. Periodically a submarine or even sub-aerial ridge was produced on which erosion laid bare the older rocks forming the core. The strata resulting from renewed deposition following submergence show overlap and overstep.

In many formations the almost bewildering varieties of contemporaneous rock types would, at first sight, appear to be accidental; but when the distribution of these facies is related to the position of the axes the seemingly haphazard variations in lithology are seen to be intimately related to continuous instability along the axial lines.

The three principal axes shown in Fig. 3 must not be regarded as single continuous folds; the Mendip Axis is clearly seen to consist of at least four anticlinal folds arranged *en echelon*, whilst the Lower Severn Axis at its northern end appears to contain at least two diverging folds.

In recurrent movement along established lines of weakness the successive fold axes are not always coincident but tend to migrate within the limits of a broad zone, though they retain a parallel alignment.

THE AXES

Lower Severn Axis.—In the unconformity between the Cambrian and Silurian rocks along the Berkeley—Tortworth fold are to be found the earliest indications of movement: during Silurian times the Lower Severn Axis may have formed a partial barrier between the Welsh Border and Bristol—Somerset basins of deposition. The Berkeley—Tortworth fold may be regarded either as a part of the Lower Severn Axis or a slightly divergent line of weakness of Malvernoid trend which continued southwards through Cattybrook and Broadfield Down to Blackdown on the Mendips. The Lower Severn Axis was active during the Old Red Sandstone earth movements and the succeeding series of Carboniferous Limestone facies changes appear to be directly attributable to

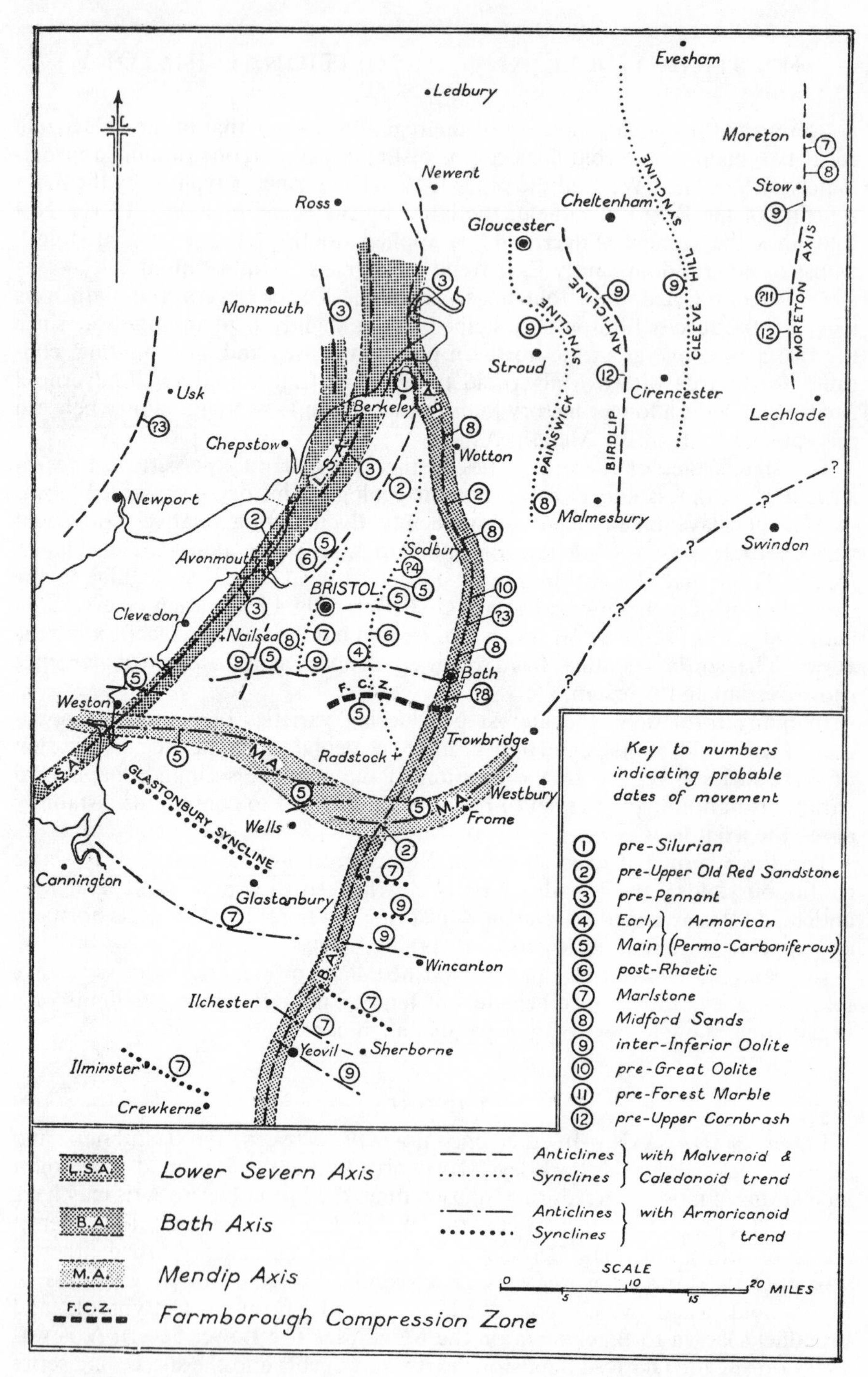

FIG. 3. *Sketch-map of the principal structure lines of the district*

movement along this line. Elevation along the axis at the end of Lower Carboniferous times probably formed a ridge which acted as the western limit of the Lower Coal Series swamp, and it was not until the end of Lower Coal Series times that this ridge, with its northern extension, was buried beneath the Pennant Sandstone.

Bath Axis.—The presence and position of the Bath Axis has been deduced largely from the evidence afforded by the facies changes in the Mesozoic strata; the Palaeozoic rocks, which would probably show similar changes, being for the most part concealed.

The Silurian rocks at Wickwar and the unconformity between the Upper Old Red Sandstone and the Silurian andesites in the Mendips suggest that the Bath Axis was operative at a very early date, yet during much of Carboniferous times the fold line seems to have exerted its major influence between the River Severn and Sodbury, beyond which it plunged southwards and had a diminishing effect on Carboniferous sedimentation.

In Mesozoic times the Bath Axis played an important part, not only in its northern section but even where it lies beneath the later Armoricanoid folds south of the Mendips. Its most striking effect is to be seen in the Upper Lias strata, which show that the seas shallowed in a belt extending to the Dorset coast. The winnowing action of the currents prevented the accumulation of the finer sediments, which were deposited in the form of clays and silts in the less disturbed waters flanking the sand-banks on the axis.

The extraordinary lithological variations of the Great Oolite rocks can also be related to movements along the axis.

It is interesting to note that both at Bath and Hotwells (Bristol) thermal waters rise to the surface. At Hotwells the water is said to have an average temperature of 73°F. and rises in the bed of the River Avon through fissured Carboniferous Limestone above the Avon Thrust (Fig. 13B).

The famous Hot Springs at Bath have a temperature of 120°F. and both natural gas and water are radioactive; the carbon dioxide-free gas contains 13 c.c. of rare gases per litre including 1·66 c.c. of helium.

Both springs are situated on or near the ancient axes where the latter are crossed by the Avon Valley, which permits an easy outlet for their waters. Elsewhere, as at Batheaston, high-temperature waters have been encountered at a comparatively shallow depth in shafts and borings.

Mendip Axis.—The formation of this fold and its relations to the earlier formed axes is discussed in Section IX which deals with the Armorican Earth Movements. South of the Mendips the parallel anticlines and synclines seen in the Mesozoic rocks may indicate the lines of buried Armorican folds. These east-west folds pitch east and west away from the deeply buried Bath Axis. Much of the intraformational folding seen in the Yeovil district is believed to be the result of movement along both Bath Axis and Armoricanoid fold lines.

The northward deflection of the Mendip Axis between Frome and Trowbridge is of considerable interest and suggests that the fold might continue north-eastwards through Swindon to the Islip Axis. The presence of such a fold might help to explain the very variable character of the Cornbrash along its outcrop, the local developments of sandy strata in the sandy Kellaways Beds, and the distribution of the Lower Greensand.

Other Axes.—In North Gloucestershire the Birdlip and Moreton axes cannot yet be dated back beyond Mesozoic times. Their direction is similar to that of the Bath Axis and they appear to plunge northwards as if pitching off the presumed north-easterly continuation of the Mendip Axis.

FAULTS

In addition to the major structures of pre-New Red Sandstone age there are many big faults, sometimes associated with folding, which affect the Mesozoic rocks: some of these, for example the Poyntington Fault, the great Wincanton-Mere Fault and, possibly, the Wanstrow Fault displace the Cretaceous rocks in the east and may be of Miocene age. Where Cretaceous rocks are absent, as in the Bristol Coalfield, the age of the faults, such as those of the Bitton Fault belt, can only be fixed as post-Great Oolite.

Many faults having a considerable throw are found in the coalfield where they may be either coincident with or cut the Armorican structures. Some have originated by posthumous movements along both reversed and normal faults of Armorican age and the post-Triassic component may either increase or decrease the amount of the original throw.

III. CAMBRIAN

THE OLDEST ROCKS so far recorded from the district are of Lower Tremadoc age and are known as the 'Breadstone Shales'. They were first described by Stanley Smith and Stubblefield in 1933 and occupy a small inlier to the east and north-east of Berkeley where they separate the Silurian rocks of Tites Point on the Severn from those of the main mass at Tortworth.

Though very poorly exposed the Breadstone Shales have yielded well-preserved trilobites indicative of the zone of *Dictyonema flabelliforme*.

The relationship to the Silurian is not clear: on the northern margin they are probably faulted against Ludlow beds; on the south they appear to be overlain unconformably by the Upper Llandovery without any trace of Ordovician strata intervening.

The significance of this great stratigraphical break lies in the fact that it may afford the first indication in our district of movement along the Lower Severn Axis (*see* pp. 8–10 and Fig. 3). The Cambrian inlier lies along one of the fold lines of the axis, and the great unconformity between the Cambrian and Silurian is probably due to folding along this line followed by erosion which removed any higher Tremadoc and later deposits from the crest of the fold prior to the deposition of the Silurian.

IV. SILURIAN

SILURIAN ROCKS CROP OUT in the Eastern Mendips and on the northern margin of the Bristol Coalfield where they occupy a number of inliers, the largest being that of Tortworth.

The predominantly sandy and clayey nature of the sediments, with a consequent feeble development of limestone, together with the presence of contemporaneous volcanic rocks in the series, affords a striking contrast to the well-known succession of the Welsh Borderland, Woolhope and Usk in which shelly limestones and coral reefs play such an important part, and it is quite possible that the Lower Severn Axis formed a partial barrier between the two areas of deposition.

The Silurian rocks fall into three main divisions:

Ludlow Series
Wenlock Series
Llandovery Series

At the top of the Ludlow Series is the well-known Ludlow Bone Bed which marks a definite break in deposition. Above this lies a group of beds known as the Downton Series which is grouped by some authorities with the Silurian, by others with the Old Red Sandstone.

TORTWORTH INLIER

The most complete succession of Silurian rocks has been established in the Tortworth Inlier where the three divisions are represented, though at the present time exposures are very limited. The base of the Llandovery is not exposed and most of the Ludlow has been cut out by the Upper Old Red Sandstone overstep (*see* Fig. 4). The three thin bands of limestone in the Wenlock—Ludlow Series have not been identified individually as Woolhope, Wenlock and Aymestry. The beds are synclinally disposed and follow round the northern rim of the Bristol Coalfield.

The general succession, based on the work of Professor S. H. Reynolds, is as follows:

		Approximate thickness in ft.
LUDLOW AND WENLOCK	Sandstones possibly of Ludlow age exposed beneath Old Red Sandstone at Horseshoe Farm, Milbury Heath	—
	Sandstones	—
	Upper Limestone Band. Red nodular limestone	—
	Shales	—
	Middle Limestone Band. Red crinoidal limestone	25
	Shales	50
	Lower Limestone Band with coral '*Hallia*'	30
LLANDOVERY	Sandstone, fossiliferous	?100
	Ashy limestone with many fossils (some Llandovery, some Wenlock)	3
	Upper Trap Band. A lava flow	60
	Thin sandstones, shales and sandy limestones with *Coelospira hemisphaerica*, *Stricklandia lirata*, *Stropheodonta* (*Leptostrophia*) *compressa*, *Dalmanites weaveri*. A prominent band of sandy limestone with corals occurs a short distance below the Trap	500
	Lower Trap Band. Intrusive	185
	Sandy micaceous shale with *Lingula symondsi* (base not seen)	—

The Upper Trap Band, a lava flow, is a microporphyritic basalt usually amygdaloidal, the amygdales being filled with calcite, chlorite or chalcedony. The rock contains little or no olivine and has a glassy groundmass. Xenocrysts of quartz are present.

The Lower Trap Band, an intrusion, is an olivine-basalt which has been subjected to widespread albitization. The rock is holocrystalline and non-porphyritic. The original olivine is now altered to chlorite (serpentine) and

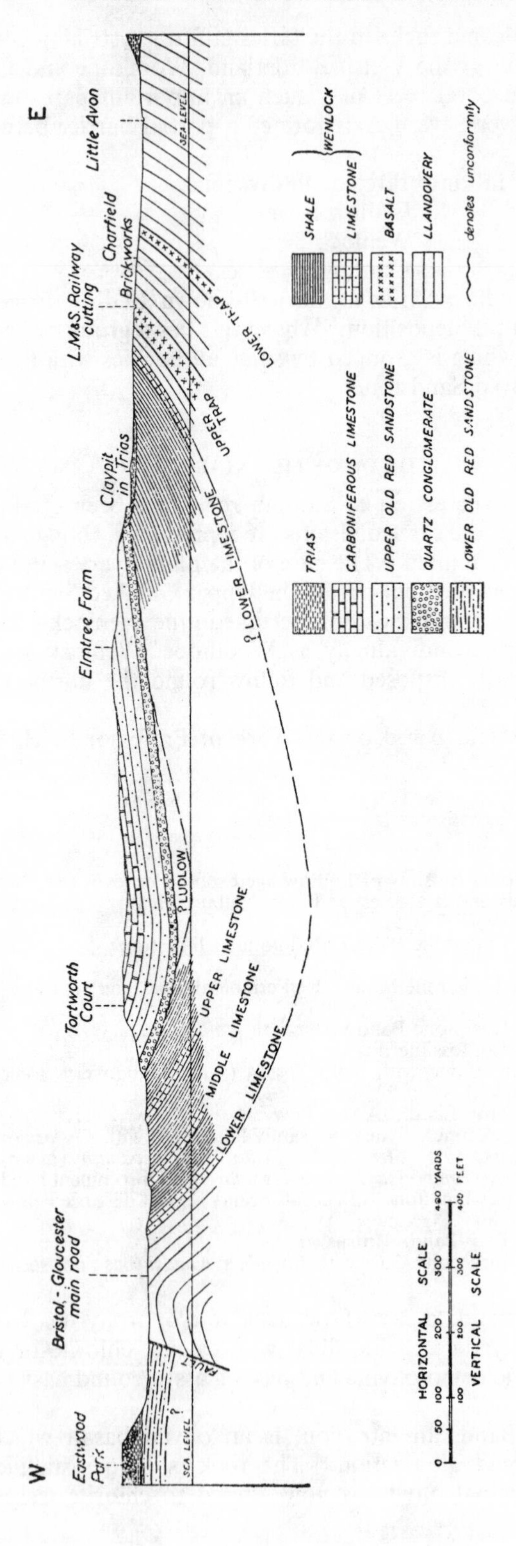

FIG. 4. *Section across the Silurian inlier at Tortworth*
(The upper part of the Wenlock Beds as shown may include some rocks of Ludlow age)

opaque oxides. The rock is amygdaloidal, the amygdales being filled with calcite or chlorite.

The relationships of the various beds may be seen from Fig. 4.

WICKWAR

West of Wickwar, in the valley of the Little Avon, there are small exposures of Wenlock. The rocks here consist of pink dolomitic siltstones and argillaceous limestones which, when fresh, have proved highly fossiliferous.

Farther north some small inliers of shales and thin decalcified sandy limestones of presumed Llandovery age crop out in the river bed.

SHARPNESS

In the Berkeley—Sharpness area Silurian rocks are known to have a considerable outcrop, but information about them is scanty owing to lack of exposures. At Tites Point on the Severn calcareous shales and sandstones occur with Ludlow fossils.

MENDIPS

In the Eastern Mendips Silurian rocks occur in the core of an anticline and are exposed through the erosion of the overlying Old Red Sandstone and Carboniferous sediments. The Silurian beds occupy a narrow belt on Beacon Hill, lying to the north-east of Shepton Mallet.

The most striking feature in the inlier is the great thickness of pyroxene-andesite which overlies Llandovery tuff and lava. It can be well studied in the large quarries of Moon's Hill and Downhead.

The general succession of beds is as follows:

		Approximate thickness in ft.
LUDLOW	Absent	—
WENLOCK	Mudstones, often very fossiliferous, with bands of highly micaceous sandstone. Typical Lower Wenlock fossils include *Horiostoma globosum*, *Cornulites serpularius*, *Acaste* [*Phacops*] *downingiae*. Exposed in rail-cuttings	120
	Pyroxene-andesite with some tuff at Moon's Hill, Sunnyhill and Downhead quarries	400
LLANDOVERY	Tuff and lava with fossils probably indicating Upper Llandovery, in Sunnyhill quarry (now overgrown)	About 110

In addition to the tuff and lava of Llandovery age, coarse ashy conglomerate was formerly exposed at two points. This material consists of blocks of andesite embedded in an ashy matrix and may indicate the site of vents from which lava and tuff were ejected.

V. OLD RED SANDSTONE

APART FROM THE BREAK shown by the Ludlow Bone Bed, sedimentation continued unchecked until it was terminated by the great earth movements at the end of Lower Old Red Sandstone times. This diastrophism was the culmination of earth movements which had gradually converted the arms of the

Silurian sea into a series of inland seas or lakes, in which sediments derived from the denudation of the surrounding high ground accumulated under rather arid conditions. The deposits include red shales, sandstones and conglomerates, whilst locally there is a considerable development of thin breccia bands known as cornstones, composed of angular bits of fine-grained limestone set in a hard sandy calcareous matrix.

The exposed succession of the Old Red Sandstone is most complete in the region to the west of the River Severn where the following subdivisions have been established:

	Approximate thickness in ft.
UPPER OLD RED SANDSTONE	
Tintern Sandstone Group. Light grey to yellow-brown sandstones with subordinate red and green marl bands. Thin dark green highly micaceous sandy shale bands are common	200 to 300
Quartz Conglomerate. Conglomerate of vein quartz, decomposed igneous rocks and occasional jaspers. The conglomerate may occur as one band or in two or three bands separated by red shale or sandstone	20 to 100
LOWER OLD RED SANDSTONE	
Brownstones. Dull grey-brown micaceous, frequently current-bedded sandstones with thin shale partings. Cornstone bands are rare	2,500
St. Maughans Group. Alternating red sandstone and marl with numerous cornstone bands. At the base is a thin limestone believed to be the equivalent of the *Psammosteus* Limestone	1,400
DOWNTON SERIES	
Raglan Marls. Red sandy marls with occasional red and green sandstones ..	1,000

The earth movements, mentioned above, were principally confined to folding along the Lower Severn Axis and, probably, the Bath Axis. Prolonged erosion of the crest of the Lower Severn Axis removed most of the Lower Old Red Sandstone and exposed the Silurian rocks at its core. Upon this erosion plane the Upper Old Red Sandstone was deposited, the basal members consisting of one or more beds of massive quartz-conglomerate which rest on the earlier formed Lower Old Red Sandstone strata and, along the axial crests, overstep onto the Silurian.

Not only is there a great depositional break but there is also an important break in the fauna. Lower Old Red Sandstone times saw the gradual extinction of the Silurian fauna and the establishment of the heavily armoured 'fish' known as ostracoderms of which *Pteraspis* and *Cephalaspis* are the most familiar. By Upper Old Red Sandstone times most of the ostracoderms had died out and the commonest fish were the enamel-scaled ganoids exemplified by *Holoptychius* and *Glyptopomus*.

WEST OF THE RIVER SEVERN

Overlooking the low ground formed by the St. Maughans group the Brownstones form the fine wooded scarp bordering the east side of the Usk Valley near Newport. Rising to nearly 1,000 ft. above sea-level at Wentwood, this scarp runs in a curving north-easterly direction to near Trellech. On the east side of the Forest of Dean the Brownstones, dipping steeply westwards, form a series of prominent north-south ridges from Mitcheldean southwards past Blakeney to Lydney.

The Quartz Conglomerate frequently makes bare crags and a well-marked feature. With the overlying Tintern Sandstones it forms high upland tracts of poor sandy soil usually devoted to forestry. Its scarp lies approximately two miles east of and roughly parallel to the Brownstone ridge and at Trellech rises to Beacon Hill, 1,003 ft. O.D., the highest point in the district. North of Trellech the great unconformity between Upper and Lower Old Red Sandstone becomes more evident as the overstep westwards by the conglomerate reduces the width of the Brownstones outcrop until, south of Mitchel Troy, near Monmouth, the conglomerate rests directly upon the St. Maughans Group. Beyond Monmouth the outcrop of the Upper Old Red Sandstone runs in an irregular narrow belt around the northern end of the Forest of Dean coalfield basin. The dips here steepen to about 40° in the limbs of the Wigpool Syncline and maintain this high angle southwards to Tidenham. In the Lydney area the outcrop is concealed for a short distance by an overstep of the Coal Measures (Fig. 9).

SHARPNESS—THORNBURY

Old Red Sandstone beds are exposed along the western flank and across the nose of the plunging Thornbury Anticline, one of the folds along the line of the Lower Severn Axis. They are also exposed at the northern end of the Bristol Coalfield in the Tortworth and Wickwar areas. At Sharpness the Downton Series has yielded the ostracoderm *Traquairaspis*. Owing to the proximity of the Lower Severn Axis the Lower Old Red Sandstone in this area is largely cut out by Upper Old Red Sandstone overstep. The Brownstones and probably most of the St. Maughans Group are missing and all that appears beneath the Quartz Conglomerate is a series of red marls with very thin sandstone bands, known as the Thornbury Beds, which lithologically resemble the Raglan Marls.

The striking nature of the overstep of the Quartz Conglomerate is shown by the fact that at Thornbury it rests upon the red marls of the Lower Old Red Sandstone, but about three miles to the east at Milbury Heath it overlies Ludlow Beds and in the Tortworth area it rests upon Wenlock strata (*see* Fig. 4).

BRISTOL

In the Bristol area the Old Red Sandstone occurs in the core of the Westbury-on-Trym anticline and in the Clevedon—Portishead ridge. In the former the beds are best exposed at the Horseshoe Bend of the Avon Gorge. Here about 350 ft. of Upper Old Red Sandstone, comprising sandstones and marls with courses of conglomerate, rest upon some 90 ft. of sandstone and marl in equal proportions, at the base of which are chocolate-red marls. The latter are comparable with the red Thornbury Beds whilst the overlying sandstone-marl series may represent the St. Maughans Group.

In the cliffs between Portishead and Clevedon compact sandstones, conglomerates and intervening marls are exposed, all of which appear to be of Upper Old Red Sandstone age. Fish remains occur, the most abundant being the scales of *Holoptychius* and *Glyptopomus*.

Where the Quartz Conglomerate and Tintern Sandstone groups cannot be separated, as in the Bristol area, the name Portishead Beds may be applied. In these beds two bands of poorly preserved plants have been found, one near the junction with the Lower Limestone Shales (Carboniferous), the other about 150 ft. lower down.

MENDIPS

Old Red Sandstone is present in the cores of the four periclines (Blackdown, Pen Hill, North Hill and Beacon Hill) and in a small inlier north of Frome. The beds, which are poorly exposed, appear to belong to the Upper Old Red Sandstone. The presence of the Quartz Conglomerate resting unconformably upon the Silurian andesites of Beacon Hill suggests that this region lies on the line of a southerly prolongation of the Bath Axis (p. 9) along which movement had occurred prior to the deposition of the Upper Old Red Sandstone.

VI. CARBONIFEROUS LIMESTONE SERIES

THE FORMATION of the Tintern Sandstones was brought to an end by a general sinking of the area so that the sea, which had lain far to the south, now spread over the whole of the Old Red Sandstone terrain, a region with little or no relief. The sediments laid down show a gradual passage from sandstone, through fossiliferous sandy limestones and shales, to limestones deposited in a clear but relatively shallow sea which throughout Carboniferous Limestone times remained deeper in the south than in the north. Besides this general north-south bathymetric increase there was variation in sea level caused by earth movement along the Lower Severn Axis and probably also along the Bath Axis, so that contemporaneous sedimentation shows striking variation in lithology in different parts of the area.

The deposits, where normal marine conditions obtained, consist of massive, frequently dark-coloured, highly fossiliferous, crinoidal limestones in which chert is often developed. Shallower water is indicated by the formation of massive dolomites: under still shallower conditions stretches of water became incompletely connected with the open sea and in these lagoons, unaffected by tides and currents, there were formed calcite-mudstones (chinastones), oolites, desiccation breccias, pseudo-breccias due to partial recrystallization of a calcareous mud, and algal limestones. Pene-contemporaneous dolomitization is frequent in these ' lagoon-phases '.

The extreme phase of shallowing towards open shore lines or current-swept shoals is shown by the lateral passage from limestone into grits, sandstones or conglomerates. The changes in thickness and lithology in different parts of the district are shown in Fig. 6.

Prior to 1905 the Carboniferous Limestone was divided into two parts, the lower shaly division being known as the ' Lower Limestone Shales ', the remaining great limestone division being termed ' Mountain Limestone '. The sandy and gritty beds now included in the Avonian were then regarded as basal members of the Millstone Grit.

In 1905 Arthur Vaughan published his classic paper *On the Palaeontological Sequence in the Carboniferous Limestone of the Bristol District*. Taking the Avon Gorge as the type section, he grouped ' Lower Limestone Shale ', ' Mountain Limestone ' and part of the ' Millstone Grit ' as the Avonian, which he subdivided into five zones based upon the coral-brachiopod assemblages present (*see* Fig. 5). A characteristic fossil was chosen as the index or zonal fossil in each case and its name given to the zone.

TABLE OF CLASSIFICATION OF THE CARBONIFEROUS LIMESTONE SERIES
(Modified from A. Vaughan)

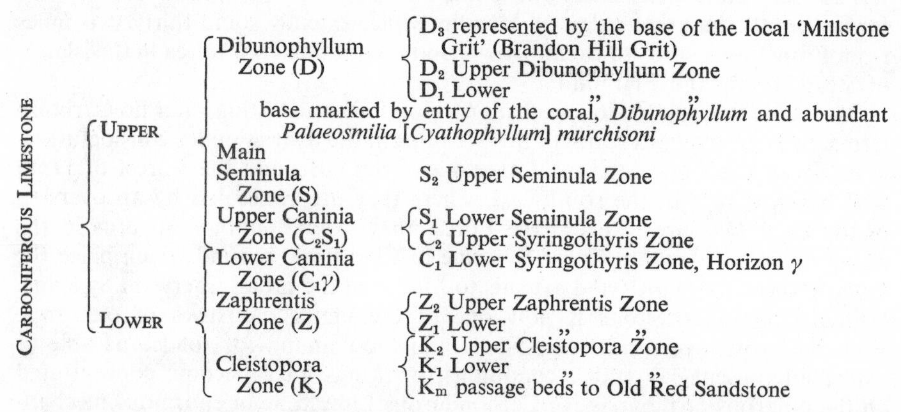

Carboniferous Limestone	Zone	Subdivisions
Upper	Dibunophyllum Zone (D)	D_3 represented by the base of the local 'Millstone Grit' (Brandon Hill Grit)
		D_2 Upper Dibunophyllum Zone
		D_1 Lower " "
	base marked by entry of the coral, *Dibunophyllum* and abundant *Palaeosmilia* [*Cyathophyllum*] *murchisoni*	
	Main Seminula Zone (S)	S_2 Upper Seminula Zone
	Upper Caninia Zone (C_2S_1)	S_1 Lower Seminula Zone
		C_2 Upper Syringothyris Zone
Lower	Lower Caninia Zone ($C_1\gamma$)	C_1 Lower Syringothyris Zone, Horizon γ
	Zaphrentis Zone (Z)	Z_2 Upper Zaphrentis Zone
		Z_1 Lower " "
	Cleistopora Zone (K)	K_2 Upper Cleistopora Zone
		K_1 Lower " "
		K_m passage beds to Old Red Sandstone

It must be pointed out that the corals and brachiopods have not the same zonal value as have free-swimming forms such as the ammonoids (goniatites) which, unfortunately, are extremely rare. For short range correlation, however, coral-brachiopod zones have proved invaluable.

In the Forest of Dean and Chepstow area, distinctive names are given to the lithological subdivisions, but in the Bristol and Mendip regions only zonal names have so far been applied.

The lithological nomenclature is as follows:

		Zone
Drybrook Sandstone		S_2
Main Limestone	Whitehead Limestone	C_2S_1
	Crease Limestone	C_1 or C_2
	Lower Dolomite	Z-C_1
Lower Limestone Shales		K

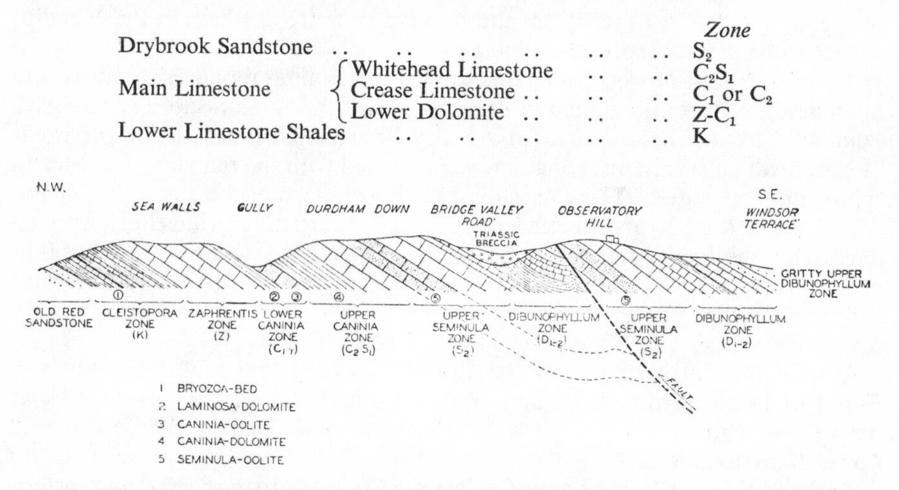

FIG. 5. *The Avon Section (right bank), showing Vaughan's zonal and lithological divisions* (Modified from S. H. Reynolds)

Carboniferous Limestone forms a rim to the northern part of the Bristol Coalfield, extending from Over north-eastwards through Almondsbury and Tytherington to Tortworth and thence southwards by Wickwar to Chipping Sodbury. Farther south it is concealed by newer rocks but reappears in several inliers at Wick and Codrington.

In the vicinity of Bristol it forms the high ground extending from Penpole Point through King's Weston to Durdham Downs and thence by Failand to

Clevedon. It further gives rise to the Clevedon—Portishead ridge. Carboniferous Limestone constitutes the dome-like uplift of Broadfield Down, and farther south the great ridge of Mendip which extends some thirty-two miles from Frome westwards to Brean Down, and is continued out to sea in the islands of Steep Holme and Flatholm.

Except for the isolated inlier of Cannington Park near Bridgwater no Carboniferous beds are exposed south of the Mendips in the district under consideration.

Rocks of the Carboniferous Limestone Series surround the Forest of Dean coal basin, except in the south-east, where they are concealed by an overstep of the Coal Measures. From the Forest they extend south-westwards in the rather narrow Tidenham Chase Syncline to Chepstow, beyond which place the outcrop turns westwards and extends to Magor in the broad Caerwent Syncline.

Quarrying of limestone is now one of the major industries of our area. With the growth of modern transport and the demand for roadstone able to withstand present-day traffic conditions, workings have become concentrated on the outcrops of the massive Carboniferous Limestone in enormous mechanized quarries whose products are widely distributed over the southern half of England. The old local stone pits working the softer Jurassic limestones have largely disappeared.

LOWER CARBONIFEROUS LIMESTONE

Cleistopora Zone (K).—In the Bristol-Sodbury area 150 to 200 ft. of sandy limestones with fish remains, thin grits and shales with spirorbid worms, ostracods and molluscs represent the passage beds (K_m), which in the Mendips appear to be greatly reduced in thickness.

At the top thin red crinoidal limestones, containing abundant polyzoa, are often developed: of these the red Bryozoa Bed of the Avon Section is a massive example. In the Bristol area above the Bryozoa Bed lies the impersistent ' Palate-Bed ', a calcareous conglomerate crowded with the remains of fish-teeth, spines and coprolites. The commonest teeth are those of the shark *Psephodus*.

The passage beds are succeeded by shales alternating with thin crinoidal limestones, the Lower Limestone Shales, which reach a thickness of over 500 ft. in the Mendip area. The limestone bands are usually highly fossiliferous, common forms being *Productus bassus, Camarotoechia mitcheldeanensis, Spiriferina octoplicata, Chonetes failandensis* and Athyrids.

Around the northern rim of the Bristol Coalfield and in the Chepstow—Forest of Dean region oolitic and crinoidal limestones, up to 150 ft. thick at the western end of the Caerwent Syncline, are developed at the base of the Lower Limestone Shales.

Zaphrentis Zone (Z) and Lower Caninia Zone ($C_1\gamma$).—In the central and eastern Mendips, where relatively deep water conditions obtained, these zones are represented mainly by dark crinoidal limestones (Z), which are thinly bedded in their lower part, overlain by similar limestones of lighter grey colour (C_1). Chert is frequently developed, especially at Horizon γ, and this is well seen in Vallis Vale and Burrington Combe.

Fossils are abundant, those of the lower thinly bedded limestones include *Spirifer clathratus* (*tornacensis*), *Leptaena analoga*, *Chonetes hardrensis* and *Schellwienella crenistria*. The simple cornute coral *Zaphrentis* occurs throughout and is very abundant at Horizon γ in association with *Caninia* which now appears for the first time.

(A 6289)

THE AVON GORGE

(A 6278)

THE HORSE-SHOE BEND OF THE WYE FROM THE WYNDCLIFF

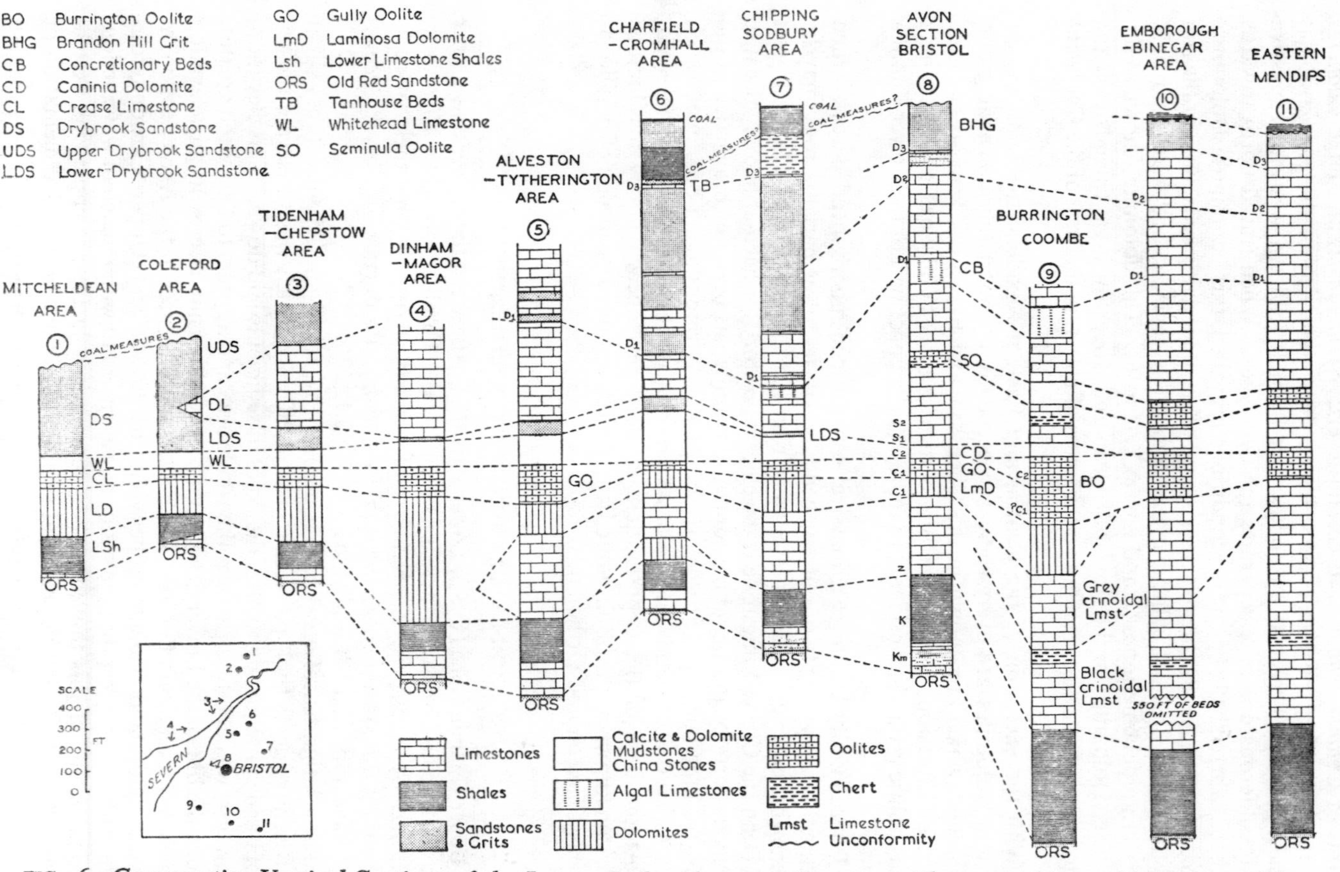

FIG. 6. *Comparative Vertical Sections of the Lower Carboniferous of Somerset, Gloucestershire and Monmouthshire*

The lighter grey crinoidal C_1 limestones, above Horizon γ, are often dolomitized but without complete obliteration of the fossils which include large forms of *Caninia cylindrica* at certain levels; *Syringothyris* and large *Chonetes* of the *comoides* type also occur. In the deep water region the grey crinoidal limestones are succeeded by oolites, but from Blackdown westwards massive unfossiliferous dolomite separates the two types. When traced north towards Bristol, where shallower water conditions prevailed, this ' Laminosa Dolomite ' becomes increasingly thick at the expense of the underlying beds, until in the rim of the north Bristol Coalfield it has completely replaced both dark and light grey crinoidal limestones (Z and lower C_1) (Fig. 6). This dolomite, known as the ' Lower Dolomite ' in the Forest of Dean and Chepstow area, extends over the remainder of our area, reaching a thickness of 600 ft. in the west of the Caerwent Syncline.

With the exception of the Central and Eastern Mendips, the Laminosa or Lower Dolomites are everywhere succeeded by a remarkably constant group of oolites which are known in the Chepstow and Forest of Dean areas as the ' Crease Limestone ', and in the Bristol district as the ' Gully or Caninia Oolite '. This oolitic group is considered to represent the upper part of the Lower Caninia Zone.

Typical Gully Oolite is a massive even-grained, poorly-bedded rock which frequently shows signs of current bedding; in its lower part the rock may be somewhat crinoidal. Thicknesses vary from 40 to 180 ft. (Fig. 6). In the Forest of Dean the Crease Limestone is the chief repository for haematite ore. Because of its uniformity and high lime content the oolite has been much quarried in the past for lime-burning. Fossils are comparatively rare, though braciopods such as *Chonetes*, Orthotetids and *Syringothyris* may occur, also the coral *Michelinia*.

At the base of the deposit there is often developed a highly fossiliferous horizon known as the ' Sub-oolite Bed ' which contains a profusion of papilionaceous *Chonetes* and Orthotetids.

UPPER CARBONIFEROUS LIMESTONE

Upper Caninia Zone (C_2S_1), Lower Part (C_2).—Between the Lower and Upper Carboniferous Limestone there is a faunal break. Familiar forms like *Michelinia, Spirifer, Syringothyris, Zaphrentis* and *Caninia* disappear and their place is taken by *Lithostrotion, Composita* [*Seminula*], Productids of the *P. hemisphaericus* type and Clisiophyllids.

The stratigraphical break also is noteworthy, for in mid-Avonian times slight earth movements took place, the general effect of which was to elevate the sea floor and consequently to alter the types of sediments laid down. This elevation, however, was not uniform over the whole area and appears to have been greatest along the line of the Lower Severn Axis. There was not necessarily any elevation above sea level along this axis, but slight non-sequences in the Avon Section, at Tytherington and Tidenham between the Lower and Upper Carboniferous Limestone do suggest that the sea floor was raised to within reach of wave action.

The results of this movement are summarized in the accompanying sketch-maps (Fig. 7). It will be seen that approximately five belts of sedimentation or facies can be distinguished in a sea which deepened away from the Lower Severn Axis, in contrast to the almost uniformly deep waters of upper C_1 times. It must, however, be emphasized that there is no hard and fast line separating adjacent facies, the lithological types of which merge into one another.

In the belt of deepest water we find massive, fossiliferous light grey limestones, and it would appear that here little or no pause took place in sedimentation between the Lower and Upper Carboniferous Limestone.

To the west and north-west is a zone in which fossiliferous white oolite, the Burrington Oolite, is developed. This facies interdigitates on its north-west margin with the Gastropod facies which includes massive grey limestones, sometimes oolitic and containing subsidiary chinastones. Gastropods are abundant, particularly *Bellerophon* and *Euomphalus*.

This facies is developed in the Holms, Western Mendips and Broadfield Down and extends as far north as Failand.

The still shallower water of the Dolomite-Chinastone facies is exemplified by the Caninia Dolomite of the Avon Section. This consists largely of mudstone alternating with limestones and fine oolites, though most of the original structure has been destroyed by subsequent dolomitization.

In the extreme shallow water of the Algal—Chinastone facies, which is known as the Whitehead Limestone west of the Severn, the prevailing rock types are pale grey calcite or dolomite mudstones, and there is often a strong development of algal limestone.

Apart from the calcareous algae *Mitcheldeania* and *Spongiostroma* the shallow water facies are very unfossiliferous. In the oolite and deeper water sediment corals such as *Cyathoclisia tabernaculum* (=*Cyathophyllum* φ) are important.

After the establishment of the five facies in C_2 times elevation of the sea floor continued so that by S_1 times the whole of our district, as far north as a line joining Henbury and Pucklechurch, was covered by a shallow lagoon-like sea in

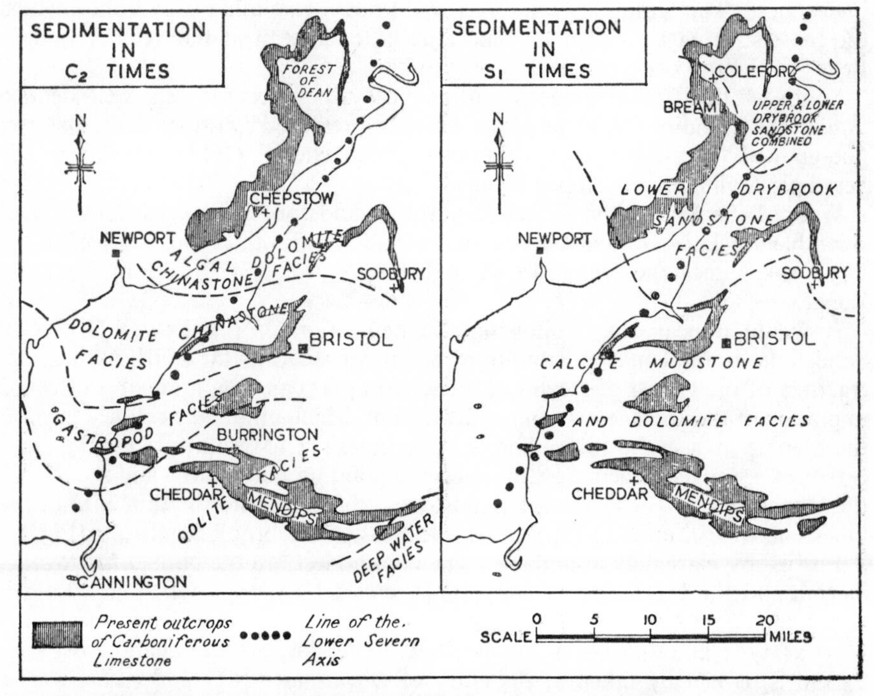

FIG. 7. *Sketch-maps showing the probable distribution of facies in C_2 and S_1 times*

which the deposits approximate to the Caninia Dolomite type. Apart from the Mendip region where white oolite gives place to dolomites and calcite mudstones, the type of rock that continued to form in S_1 times differs little from that of C_2; the dividing line between C_2 and S_1 is therefore drawn on fossil evidence at the first entry of the coral *Lithostrotion martini*.

Meanwhile the elevation of mid-Avonian times appears to have affected the great land mass, known as St. George's Land, which lay to the north and north-west of the region (*see* British Regional Geology: Central England, Second Edition, Fig. 6, p. 28). From this land area the rivers, rejuvenated by uplift, swept down great quantities of sand into the Carboniferous sea. These sands appear to have reached our district towards the end of C_2 or the beginning of S_1 times. Fig. 7 shows the approximate distribution of this sand deposit which has its most southerly extension along the line of the Lower Severn Axis where the shallower water lay.

The sandstone with subordinate shale bands is known as the Lower Drybrook Sandstone or Chepstow Grit: thickening rapidly northwards through the northern end of the Bristol Coalfield and the Chepstow and Forest of Dean areas it reaches a thickness of 200 ft. in the Bream—Milkwall district before merging with the Upper Drybrook Sandstone (Fig. 6).

In the isolated inlier of Carboniferous Limestone at Cannington Park, near Bridgwater, oolitic and crinoidal limestones occur which contain fossils indicative of the Upper Caninia Zone.

Main Seminula Zone (S_2).—The beds of this zone show the same lithological types as in the preceding zone and were evidently deposited under much the same lagoon conditions. There is a wide variety of rock types including coral limestones full of *Lithostrotion*, oolites and pisolites, chinastones and algal limestones. The seminula Oolite is a well known example of the oolites whilst the most striking type of algal limestone is to be seen in the 'Concretionary Beds' at the top of S_2 in the Bristol district.

South of the Bristol area the lithological types become less well defined until in the Mendips the whole of the zone is represented by rather dark, massive, fine-grained limestones often containing much chert. Oolites similar to the Seminula Oolite are developed locally.

West of the Severn the Lower Drybrook Sandstone is succeeded by a considerable thickness of massive, splintery and oolitic limestone known as the Drybrook Limestone which seems to belong entirely to the Main Seminula Zone.

It would appear that, following the deposition of the Lower Drybrook Sandstone, normal marine conditions again prevailed as far north as the central area of the Forest of Dean until renewed uplift caused a gradual southward migration of the arenaceous zone of deposition, which ultimately reached beyond the Mendip area in the succeeding D Zone times. The resulting general picture is that of a wedge-shaped mass of limestone pointing northwards and separating the Upper and Lower Drybrook Sandstones which, beyond the thin edge of the limestone wedge, unite to form one great mass of Drybrook Sandstone (Fig. 6).

Fossils are extremely abundant. The commonest are the coral *Lithostrotion martini* and the brachiopod *Composita* [*Seminula*] *ficoidea*. Other well-known forms include *Chonetes papilionaceus*, Productids of the *P. corrugato-hemis-phericus* type and the coral *Syringopora*. The line of demarcation between S_1 and S_2 is usually taken at the entry of *Davidsonina* [*Cyrtina*] *carbonaria*, a form which may be locally abundant as at Wickwar and in the Forest of Dean.

Dibunophyllum Zone (D).—Arenaceous conditions which started in S times in the Forest of Dean appear at successively higher horizons when traced southwards (Fig. 6). Thus at Tytherington and Wickwar practically all of D_1, and at Wick Rocks most of D_2 are represented by sandstone which in the Avon section does not appear until the top of D_2. In the Mendips the sandy conditions did not set in until D_3, so that here we have the greatest calcareous development of the D Zone (approximately 750 ft.). An almost complete succession from S to the top of D is afforded by the great Cook's Wood Quarries, four miles north-east of Shepton Mallet.

In contrast to the rather dark, fine-grained rocks of the Seminula Zone the D Zone comprises coarsely oolitic and foraminiferal limestones with a development of thin shales and 'rubbly beds' (algal limestones and pseudobreccias) towards the top.

The sandy facies of this zone will be discussed in the chapter dealing with the 'Millstone Grit'.

The D beds are highly fossiliferous. Corals include *Palaeosmilia* [*Cyathophyllum*] *murchisoni*, *Dibunophyllum* of the *turbinatum* type, and *Chaetetes septosus* in the lower part (D_1) whilst in the upper part (D_2) *Palaeosmilia* [*Cyathophyllum*] *regium* and *Lonsdaleia floriformis* are characteristic. *Lithostrotion martini* is now represented by *L. junceum* which has smaller corallites, and brachiopods include Productids of the *semireticulatus* and *giganteus* types.

VOLCANIC ROCKS

At several points in the Bristol area volcanic rocks are associated with Carboniferous beds. At Woodspring and Spring Cove, near Weston-super-Mare, Uphill, Goblin Combe and near Tickenham lavas of olivine-basalt type are present. In addition, at Woodspring and Goblin Combe there are thick beds of calcareous ash.

At Spring Cove the basalt forms part of a submarine lava-flow. This in places shows rough pillow-structure and enclosed lumps of red oolitic limestone. In the centre of this exposure cindery lava is mixed with broken limestone fragments, and apparently represents a fluxion-tuff.

These volcanic rocks are not all developed at the same level: that of Spring Cove is associated with the Laminosa Dolomite (C_1) whilst the remainder occur at a lower level in beds of Horizon γ age. This volcanic episode is probably connected with the start of the mid-Avonian earth movements and it is significant that the rocks occur close to or actually upon the line of the Lower Severn Axis.

VII. 'MILLSTONE GRIT'

IN THE TYPE AREA of East Lancashire and West Yorkshire the Millstone Grit is essentially a deltaic deposit comprising several thousand feet of sandstone, grits and shales which separate the Carboniferous Limestone from the productive Coal Measures.

In the region here described the two latter groups are separated in a similar manner by a considerable thickness of sandstone, and it is not surprising that this sandstone was mapped as Millstone Grit.

Later investigation, however, of the fauna of certain thin limestone bands within the sandstone showed conclusively that most, if not all, of this 'Millstone Grit' is in fact a sandy diachronous facies of the Carboniferous Limestone.

As such it is mapped as a separate formation under the names of Upper Drybrook Sandstone or Brandon Hill Grit.

The Millstone Grit of the type Pennine area contains four goniatite zones: these are, in ascending order, the Eumorphoceras Zone (E), Homoceras Zone (H), Reticuloceras Zone (R) and part of the Gastrioceras Zone (G), all of which are post-Avonian.

In Yorkshire, the type area of the Millstone Grit, its upper limit is drawn at the top of the Rough Rock, a massive grit which maintains its characters over a wide area.

In the present area, however, there is no such well-defined rock band and the upper boundary lies somewhere within a group of extremely variable shales and sandstones which form a part of the local Lower Coal Series. Owing to the almost complete absence of goniatites in the beds between the Lower Carboniferous grits and the Ashton Vale Marine Band (*see* Coal Measures section) it is not known what proportion of these strata should be assigned to the Millstone Grit.

So far the only definite proof of the presence of beds of equivalent age to the Millstone Grit of the North of England is provided by the occurrence of *Gastrioceras cancellatum* (Lower G Zone) in a mass of faulted shale at Vobster.

UPPER DRYBROOK SANDSTONE AND BRANDON HILL GRIT

No precise age can be assigned to the fine-grained Upper Drybrook Sandstone which in the Forest of Dean rests, to a thickness of 350 ft., on the Drybrook Limestone (S_2) and is overlain unconformably by the Trenchard Group of the Coal Measures, but it is usually considered to be the sandy equivalent of Upper Avonian limestones which are developed farther to the south.

In the exposed eastern limb of the Bristol Coalfield there is positive evidence of the Lower Carboniferous age of the Upper Drybrook Sandstone. Here at the top of some 900 ft. of sandstones is a group of thin sandy limestones known as the Tanhouse Beds, yielding a striking fauna which includes *Zaphrentis*, *Fasciculophyllum*, *Lingula*, spinose Productids and, most important of all, the goniatite *Neoglyphioceras*. This fauna definitely places the Tanhouse Beds and underlying Upper Drybrook Sandstone in the Lower Carboniferous.

At Wick, farther south, some 500 ft. of shale with grit bands separate the presumed equivalent of the Ashton Vale Marine Band from the grits and limestones of Lower Carboniferous age.

At Brandon Hill, Bristol, 600 ft. of reddish grits with thin calcareous bands containing *Productus* (*Buxtonia*) *scabriculus* succeed D_2 limestones. It is interesting to note how the spinose Productids appear to have flourished in upper Avonian times whenever sandy conditions set in.

In the Mendips and in the Broadfield Down area Avonian limestones are succeeded by fine-grained grits, and in the Eastern Mendips quarrying operations showed D_2 limestones passing up through sandy limestones containing *Chonetes politus* and spinose Productids into grits 80 to 100 ft. thick. Some 60 ft. above these grits the goniatite *Gastrioceras subcrenatum* has been found.

Certain very hard fine-grained grit bands in the formation are crushed to produce an excellent top dressing for roads. At the present time this 'quartzite' is quarried at various places in the Mendips, on Broadfield Down and at Cromhall at the northern end of the Bristol coalfield.

VIII. COAL MEASURES

THE WORKING OF COAL in the Bristol, Somerset and Forest of Dean areas is of great antiquity and may date back to Roman times. Coal working in the Kingswood district of Bristol is mentioned in the Great Pipe Roll of 1223, but it was not until after Kingswood Chase had passed out of royal hands in 1564 that coal mining became a thriving industry, and flourished in the Bristol district until the early part of the present century, reaching its peak period between 1870 and 1890.

Coal mining in the royal Forest of Dean certainly goes back to before 1282, the working of the leases or ' gales ' being carried on by the Free Miners.

GENERAL METHODS OF WORKING

In early times coal was dug mainly for use by smiths and lime-burners, the public being prejudiced against it as domestic fuel, but with the increasing shortage of wood in Tudor times its use became essential.

The early workings were sited in places where the coal cropped out and could be won by shallow excavations or by pits and levels. In the Forest of Dean the whole coalfield is exposed so that workings developed in belts along the crops. In the case of Bristol and Somerset only about 27 per cent of the field is exposed, the remainder being concealed by Trias and later deposits. The earliest workings comprised shallow pits whose development was limited by drainage and ventilation problems. In the Forest of Dean much coal was won by adit levels which provided a natural drainage.

For many years the hand windlass or horse drum was the sole method of winding coal until at about the middle of the eighteenth century the steam engine slowly came into use. With improved machinery deeper mining became practicable and by about 1800 the average depth of the pits was 140 to 160 yds. At the present time Braysdown (1,865 ft.) and Mendip (Strap) Pit, near Stratton on the Fosse (1,834 ft.) are the deepest shafts.

Long-wall working with continuous or stepped face is almost universal, an exception being the pillar-and-stall method in the thick basal seam of the Coalpit Heath—Parkfield district. In the steep or vertical seams of the Nettlebridge and Vobster areas methods resembling the stoping in metal mines were adopted.

THE TYPES OF COALS

The coals of the Bristol—Somerset area and the Forest of Dean are essentially bituminous, the majority of them having strong coking properties, and over 40 per cent of the output of the Bristol—Somerset area is used by the gas industry. In the Forest of Dean the lower series provides gas-making and long-flame steam coals whilst the middle series furnishes true house coals.

A factor that greatly contributes to the safety and ease of working in both coalfields is the almost complete absence of firedamp in the mines and, with a few exceptions, naked light working is universal.

CONDITIONS OF FORMATION OF THE COAL MEASURES

The continued uplift that had been taking place during the latter part of Lower Carboniferous times finally converted most of the region into a land area, but between the diverging arms of the Lower Severn and Bath axes lay a great stretch of low ground whose surface was seldom much above the level of the sea, which now lay far to the south. This depression, into which the rivers from the higher ground discharged their sediments, was occupied by a vast swamp. Here flourished the great forests whose rotting debris accumulated as the thick layers of peat which ultimately formed the coal seams.

The climate of the period appears to have been warm and with high perennial rainfall so that in the low-lying areas a wet substratum with a high water-table was permanently maintained. This produced stagnant swamp conditions in which aerobic decay of the peat was arrested. In the more elevated regions bordering the swamp, where the water-table lay below the surface of the ground, downward percolation of the rain water would bring in new supplies of oxygen for bacterial growth and at the same time remove the humic acids produced by fermentation. Under these conditions decomposition of dead vegetation would proceed until nothing remained but the insoluble mineral residues, all the other products having been removed in solution or liberated as gas.

The downward movement of the acid-charged waters hastened the decomposition of the underlying rocks and produced lateritic soils of a dominantly red colour. On transport of this soil to the swamp area the red colour would be changed to grey or black by reduction of the ferric oxides.

The higher ground along the Lower Severn Axis probably formed the western margin of the swamp: its eastern boundary may have coincided with the Bath Axis for a distance as far south as the Sodbury area (*see* Fig. 8), but farther to the south the older rocks composing the ridge plunged beneath the swamp which probably extended into west Wiltshire. These conditions persisted throughout Lower Coal Series times, with minor oscillations permitting the temporary incursion of the sea over the swamp region. Towards the end of this period, general uplift with folding and erosion was followed by a change in sedimentation over a wide area. Marine incursions ceased and in place of shales, fireclays and coal seams, an enormous thickness of coarse, grey, current-bedded, felspathic sandstone or grit known as the Pennant was laid down.

In the Forest of Dean and North Bristol coalfields a considerable thickness (up to 500 ft.) of red measures, conglomerates, 'espleys' and fireclays lies beneath the Pennant Sandstone and appears to thicken against the flanks of the Lower Severn Axis. It is thought that the uplift caused rejuvenation of the rivers flowing off the high ground of St. George's Land to the north and north-west, and that they deposited a huge deltaic spread of arenaceous sediment both in South Wales and in our present district. From time to time there was local silting up of the basins which allowed the establishment of swamp conditions, so that coal seams of limited extent were formed. The sandy sediments filled up all existing areas of low ground and, spreading over the ridges formed by the Lower Severn and Bath Axes, overstepped onto earlier formations. Fig. 8 shows diagrammatically the formations on which the arenaceous middle division of the Coal Measures (or more strictly beds of the Phillipsi Zone) is believed to rest. When the rivers had reached their base level the rush of sand decreased, swampy conditions were re-established on the top of the delta and the Upper Coal Series was laid down.

In contrast with the Lower Coal Series, the Upper Series is marked by the occurrence of red or barren measures whose formation is frequently ascribed to the onset of arid or semi-arid conditions. In our district, however, the presence of thick fireclays and red measures with poorly preserved plants and

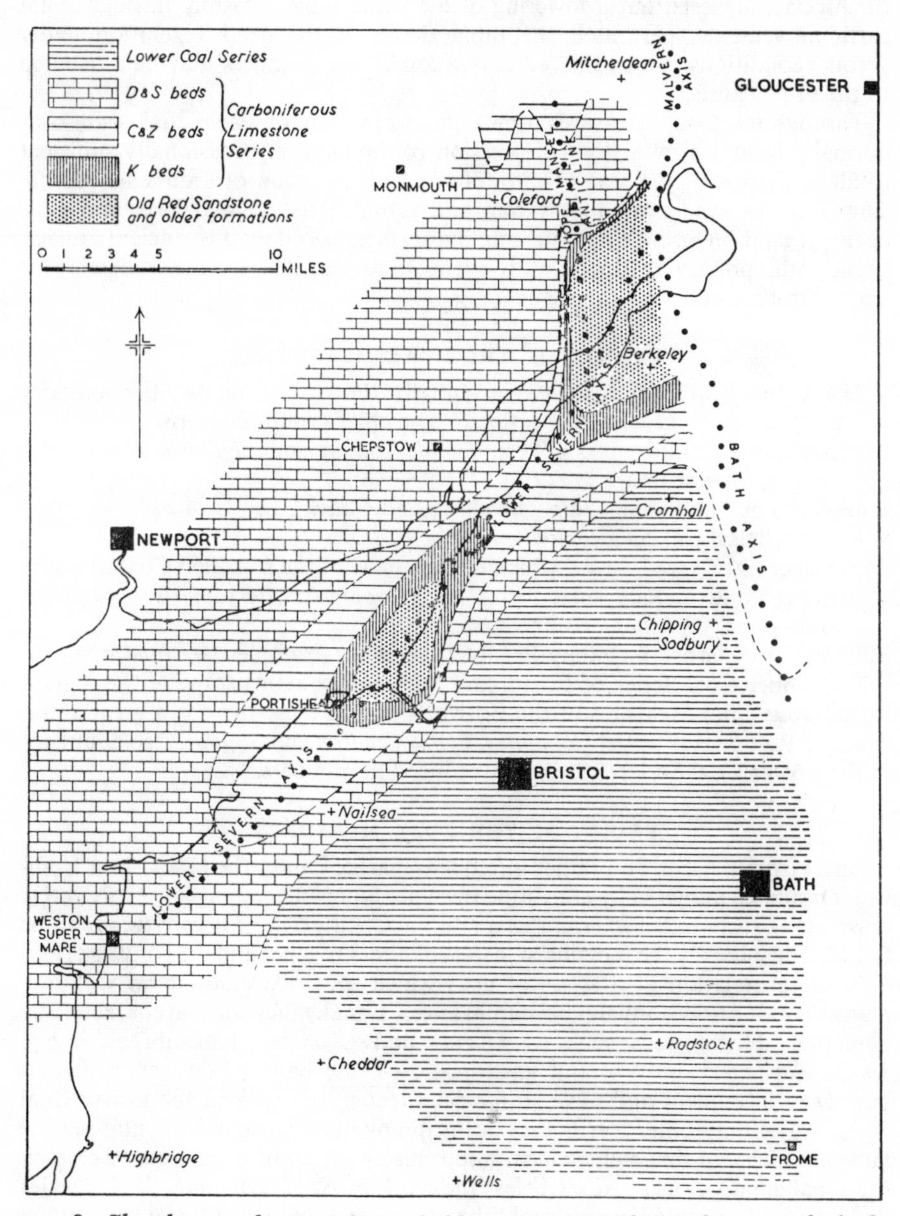

FIG. 8. *Sketch-map showing the probable outcrops at the surface on which the Pennant Series was deposited*

non-marine lamellibranchs indicates that there was still sufficient rainfall to support plants and freshwater shells. Yet the fact that no coal formed above the fireclay suggests that a lowering of the water-table, possibly through slight earth movements, permitted the rapid decay of the dead vegetation under aerobic conditions, whilst the red coloration of the measures may be attributed to the same cause.

Throughout Coal Measures times the formation of each coal seam was normally followed by a slight depression of the swamp, occasionally sufficient to allow ingress of the sea. There followed a succession of sediments passing from mud to sand until the swamp had resumed its original level and once again vegetation grew upon its muddy surface. Today this ancient muddy ' soil ', still preserving traces of rootlets, is represented by the underclay or seat-earth that underlies the seam.

PLANTS OF THE COAL MEASURES

The Upper Carboniferous was essentially the age of plants, the majority of which belong to genera now extinct. The chief groups comprise:

Lycopodiales or ' club-mosses,' e.g. *Lepidodendron* and *Sigillaria* which were the great forest trees;

Equisetales or ' horse-tails,' e.g. *Annularia* and *Calamites*;

Sphenophyllales, e.g. *Sphenophyllum*;

Pteridosperms or ' seed-ferns ' which include most of the so-called Coal Measure ' ferns ' and include such forms as *Neuropteris*, *Alethopteris*, *Linopteris*, *Mariopteris*, *Sphenopteris* and *Lonchopteris*;

Filicales, ' tree-ferns ' including Pecopterids, as for example *Asterotheca*.

The Upper Coal Series of Bristol and Somerset contains some of the highest fossiliferous Coal Measures of the British Isles. In these there is a great abundance of Pecopterids whilst *Calamites*, *Lepidodendron* and *Sigillaria*, so abundant in the Lower Coal Series, are greatly reduced in numbers.

FAUNA OF THE COAL MEASURES

Apart from the thin and rather infrequent marine bands, the brackish or freshwater molluscs numerically constitute the chief faunal assemblages. More rarely crustaceans such as *Euestheria*, *Leaia* and the Cheliceratan *Eurypterus*, are to be found, whilst locally the remains of insects like cockroaches and dragonflies occur.

In the correlation of a series of beds which show extreme lateral variation marine bands provide invaluable datum lines. Usually they contain characteristic goniatites, brachiopods such as *Lingula* and *Chonetes*, lamellibranchs, e.g. *Dunbarella* [*Pterinopecten*] and gastropods. These bands, however, are comparatively infrequent and have so far been recognized only in the Lower Coal Series. The only other fossils that occur in any abundance are the non-marine lamellibranchs, at first sight a most unpromising group of organisms to employ for zonal subdivisions. Nevertheless the work of A. E. Trueman, J. H. Davies and others has resulted in the establishment of six zones which have been found to have a wide application.

These zones are:

6. Zone of *Anthraconauta tenus*
5. ,, ,, *phillipsi*
4. *Anthraconaia pulchra* and *Anthracosia similis*
3. ,, *modiolaris*
2. *Carbonicola communis*
1. *Anthraconaia lenisulcata*

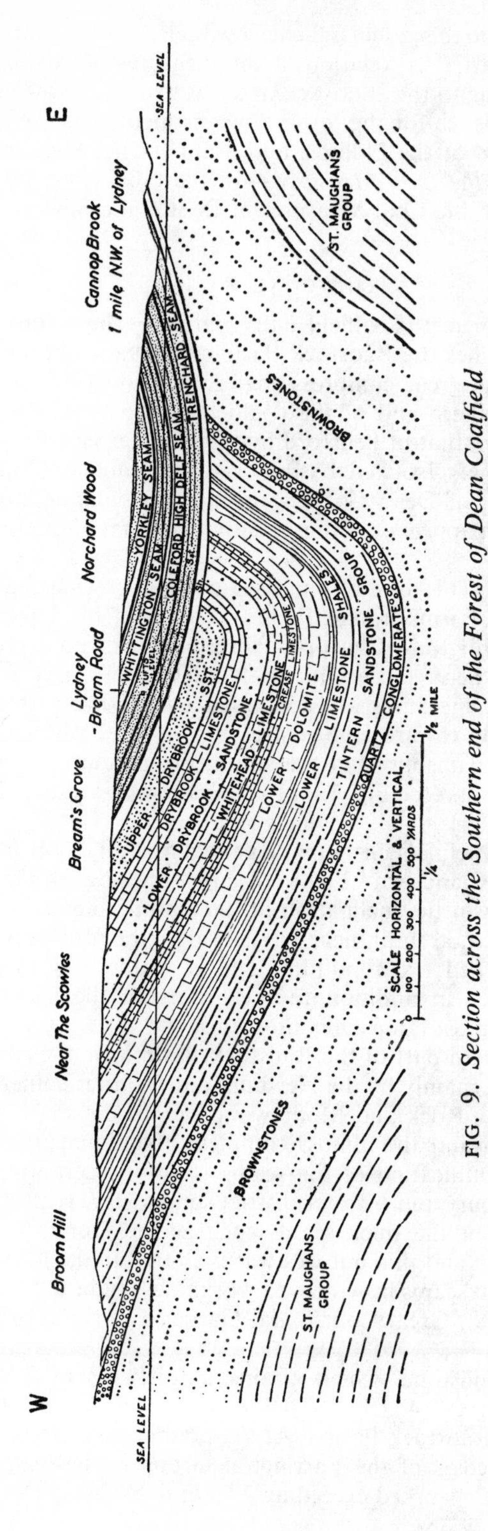

FIG. 9. *Section across the Southern end of the Forest of Dean Coalfield*

The application of this zonal scheme by L. R. Moore and A. E. Trueman has resulted in a partial correlation of the measures of our district, as shown in Fig. 10; but owing to the almost complete cessation of working in the Lower Coal Series the evidence for the lower zones is incomplete, while in the higher strata the separation of the Phillipsi and Tenuis zones is difficult to establish.

Subdivisions of the Coal Measures.—In the table (Fig. 10) are set out the main subdivisions of the Coal Measures of Bristol and Somerset.

THE COAL BASINS

The Bristol—Somerset Coalfield falls naturally into four distinct areas: at the southern end lies the Radstock Basin separated from the Pensford Basin on the north by the great compressional zone known as the 'Farmborough Fault.' At the northern end of the coalfield is the Parkfield—Coalpit Heath Basin separated from that of Pensford by the complex east-west fold belt of the Kingswood Anticline. Isolated basins occur at Nailsea, Clapton and Avonmouth. The Forest of Dean Coalfield occupies a separate structural basin in which the succession appears to differ greatly from that of the Bristol—Somerset Coalfield.

Radstock Basin.—This basin comprises a roughly U-shaped syncline lying to the south of the Farmborough Fault. A little of the Upper Coal Series is exposed in the Farrington—Clutton—Timsbury area, and a considerable tract of the Lower Coal Series occurs in the Nettlebridge Valley, but for the most part the productive measures are concealed by Mesozoic strata. There is a general moderate dip towards the central axis of the basin which lies in a line with Radstock and Timsbury but the strata, throughout, are much broken by east-west overlap faults (*see* Fig. 13) of which the well-known 'Radstock Slide' is an example (Fig. 11).

Parallel to the synclinal axis runs a belt of roughly N-S faults termed the '100-Fathom' or 'Clandown' Fault. Against the ridge of the Mendips at the south end of the basin the inclination of the strata increases when traced eastwards from Moorewood until, near Nettlebridge, the measures become vertical and finally overturned; a condition that is maintained through Newbury, Mells and Vobster. In addition to this inversion the incompetent Vobster measures display almost fantastic contortions.

Only in the southern part of the Radstock Basin have the coals of the Lower Series been worked, mainly by the Newbury and Vobster collieries in the south-east and in the New Rock and Moorewood pits to the south-west. Owing to the intense faulting and the almost complete abandonment of the workings, correlation and identification of the seams is very uncertain between the two areas. In the Newbury and Vobster district some twelve seams were extensively worked, but some of the thick seams such as the Dungy Drift and Coking Coals appear to split and thin out westwards so that in the New Rock—Moorewood area only eight seams have proved workable. In both regions the Perrink, Main Coal (Callows), Great Course and Garden Course have been extensively mined.

The Pennant Sandstone, which attains a thickness of 2,500 ft. or more, is succeeded by some 1,400 ft. of the Upper Coal Series which occupy the central part of the Radstock Basin. At the present time almost all the working is confined to the coals of the Farrington Group. The seams are thin, only three of the five coals worked exceeding 2 ft. in thickness. The six seams of the

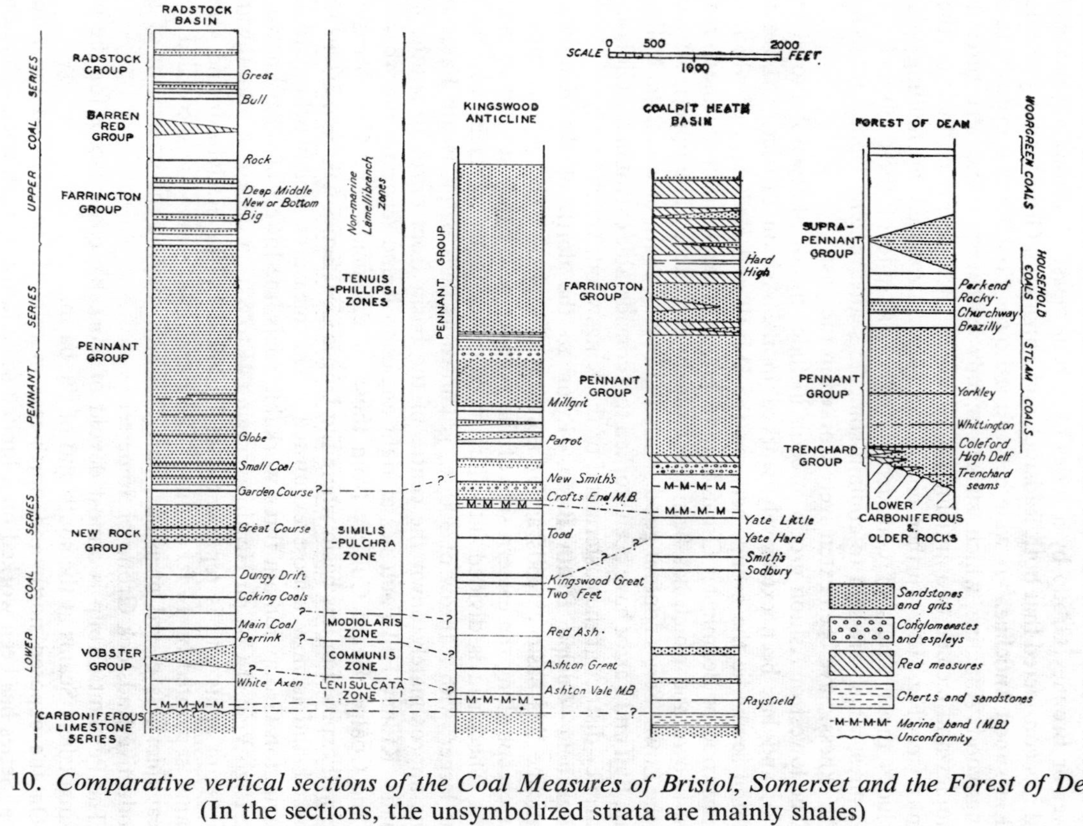

FIG. 10. *Comparative vertical sections of the Coal Measures of Bristol, Somerset and the Forest of Dean*
(In the sections, the unsymbolized strata are mainly shales)

once extensively mined Radstock Group are now virtually exhausted. When traced northwards there is a tendency for the seams to split and to deteriorate in quality, so that coals in the Pensford Basin to the north, believed to be the equivalents of those at Radstock, are thinner and dirtier.

Pensford Basin.—Although this basin covers a wide area, little is known of the nature or succession of the measures except in the region around Pensford and Bromley Collieries. Here an upper or Pensford Group is separated from a lower or Bromley Group by a series of barren measures containing red shales and it is considered that both Radstock and Farrington Groups are represented.

Kingswood Anticline.—A wide belt of the Lower Coal Series is exposed in the Kingswood Anticline which strikes mainly east-west. The structures are complex and include two anticlinal folds which pitch steeply on their northern flanks (*see* Fig. 12): further complication is introduced by faulting which includes thrust faults of considerable size. In spite of these obstacles the measures, which are said to contain some 25 seams ranging from 1 ft. to 6 ft. in thickness, have been extensively worked in the past.

The lowest or Ashton group of coals includes the well-known Ashton Great Vein, and has been extensively worked in the Ashton district. Above the Ashton seams lie the group, between the Doxall and Red Ash, of which the Kingswood or Bedminster Great Vein (averaging over 4½ ft. in thickness) is the best-known and which has been most widely exploited. The uppermost coals of the Lower Series contain good smith and coking coals, of which the Millgrit, Rag, Buff and Parrot have been worked to a considerable extent in the Oldland—Warmley district at the eastern end of the Kingswood Anticline.

Parkfield—Coalpit Heath Basin.—Lying to the north of the Kingswood Anticline this basin extends as far north as Cromhall. The general dips are low except along the eastern side of the syncline where they steepen to nearly 40°. The basin is divided into four more or less equal parts by two faults. The larger, with a throw of 300 ft., is known as the Coalpit Heath Fault and runs approximately down the centre of the basin from north to south; the smaller Kidney Hill Fault lies at right angles to it and separates the workings of the Coalpit Heath Colliery from those of Parkfield. The Coal Measures are well exposed in this basin where the Upper Coal Series has been extensively worked and is now almost exhausted. The measures which belong to the Farrington Group contain three workable coals, the lowest of them known as the High Vein at Coalpit Heath, averaging 4½ to 5 ft. in thickness. Southwards this seam splits and is represented at Parkfield by the Hollybush and Great Seams, separated by 1½ ft. of dirt. The Farrington seams are succeeded by a great thickness of red measures, part of which may be the equivalent of the productive Radstock Group of Somerset.

The Pennant Group is almost devoid of workable coals except for the two Mangotsfield Seams at the south end of the basin.

On the exposed north and north-east margin of the coalfield the Lower Coal Series has been worked on a limited scale in the Yate district. Here only two thin seams were mined to any extent and, when compared with the Kingswood succession, the Lower Coal Series of Yate shows a remarkable attenuation in thickness and a great reduction in number of workable coals.

Nailsea Basin.—Owing to the final abandoment between 1880 and 1890 of the coal workings in this basin, due to heavily watered measures and the rather inferior nature of the coal, there is little available information regarding the succession. A maximum thickness of about 800 ft. of Pennant-like sandstone rests on a series of shales, coals and subordinate sandstones which reach a thickness of about 1,000 ft. Two seams are known from the Pennant but only one of these, Grace's Seam (3 ft. thick), was worked. In the underlying measures some 12 seams are recorded; of these only White's Top ($3\frac{1}{2}$ ft.) and the Dog ($2\frac{3}{4}$ ft.) were mined to any extent.

Clapton Basin.—Little is known of the structure and sequence of this small and almost concealed basin, but it is believed that the Coal Measures fall within the Pennant Series.

Avonmouth Basin.—The full extent of this basin is not known since it lies partly under the River Severn. Borings north of Avonmouth have proved two seams believed to correspond to the Hollybush and Great Veins of Parkfield. These coals overlie Pennant Sandstone which forms the greater part of the Coal Measures proved in the Severn Tunnel. The Lower Coal Series is probably absent or, at the most, extremely thin in this region of the Lower Severn Axis, but away from this line the lower measures appear to thicken.

Forest of Dean Basin.—In contrast with the basins of the Somerset and Bristol area, that of the Forest of Dean is completely exposed and covers an area of some 34 square miles. Folding along roughly north-south lines has given rise to the Main Basin in the east and the shallow asymmetric Worcester Syncline in the west separated from one another by the five-mile-long Cannop Fault Belt. This zone of faulting trends NNW-SSE, and includes up to 25 faults, with throws not greater than 55 ft. In the centre of the Main Basin the measures are almost flat, but on its eastern side the Staple Edge Monocline upfolds the strata a maximum vertical distance of 700 ft.

The lowest measures, termed the Trenchard Group, vary from 50 to 400 ft. in thickness and everywhere rest unconformably upon older formations (*see* Fig. 9). In the Coleford area they include two seams which, farther south-east, come together to form the Trenchard Seam $4\frac{1}{2}$ ft. in thickness. South-west of a line drawn roughly NW-SE through Coleford the Trenchard Group consists mainly of grey sandstones, but to the north-west it passes into barren red shales and mudstones.

At the base of the Pennant Group lies the Coleford High Delf Seam, which averages from $3\frac{1}{2}$ to 5 ft. in thickness. This, the most important seam in the coalfield, supplies 97 per cent of the total output. Two other seams in the Pennant, the Whittington and Yorkley, are only workable over limited areas.

In the lower part of the Supra Pennant Group eight workable coals are present. Many of the seams, however, are split into layers or leats by soft mudstone partings and can usually be mined only where two or more leats have run together.

In the Trenchard and Pennant coals there occur ' wants ' or ' washouts ' which are clearly the result of contemporaneous stream erosion. The ' Horse ' and ' Little Horse ' in the Coleford High Delf of the Worcester Syncline are good examples of this phenomenon and extend for distances of $1\frac{1}{2}$ miles with an average width of 150 and 50 yards respectively.

IX. ARMORICAN EARTH MOVEMENTS

THE PRECURSORY MOVEMENTS which had been going on during Carboniferous times culminated in one of the greatest periods of earth movement that the world has known. Great earth pressures elevated a system of mountain chains (the Altaides of Suess) which stretched across Central Europe to Asia. That part of the mountain belt which ran through southern Ireland, south-west England and northern France is called the Armorican Chain.

The ' Armorican front ' or northern limit of the mountain belt coincides roughly with the Mendip Axis (Fig. 3, p. 8). South of this line there is isoclinal folding and great over-thrusting; in the ' Armorican foreland ' to the north, the movements were less violent.

In our present district the Armorican earth storm can be likened to a series of great storm waves approaching a coast-line in which lay a deep inlet protected by two promontories. On this analogy the promontories are represented by the Lower Severn and Bath axes which plunge southwards beneath the waves of the Armorican swell, while the basin of the Bristol—Somerset Coalfield may be likened to the sheltered inlet at the head of the gulf. The east-west storm waves would continue with less frequency as a ground swell up the central waters, gradually changing to ripples at the head of the inlet. Where the promontories are struck head-on, the waves would be violently checked, but along the inner margins of the headlands they would be deflected so as to strike the sides of the inlet obliquely.

Thus north of the Mendip Axis the east-west folds are developed across the centre of the coalfield, but against the flank of the Lower Severn Axis the folds appear to be rotated and to become aligned with the general direction of the Axis. South of the Mendips the ancient mountains are largely buried by later rocks but the intensity of the earth movements is demonstrated by their folded and shattered stumps which appear in the Quantocks, North Devon and West Somerset. One effect of tremendous thrust faulting is the northward translation of Culm-type Carboniferous sediments so that they now lie within a relatively short distance of the normal marine limestones of Cannington.

There is evidence that, prior to the oncoming of the main folding movements directed from the south, there was closure of the arms of the Lower Severn and Bath axes with the resulting formation of the Bristol—Somerset Coalfield synclinal and its associated minor Malvernoid folds.

During the main period of earth movement which followed, the main compressive forces acted from the south or south-east. The largest visible structure produced was the Mendip ridge, which consists of four or more periclines arranged *en échelon*, the axes of which run approximately east-west (Fig. 3); the north-east deflection of the Mendip Axis in the Frome area is suggested by the form of the sub-Triassic surface. Most of the periclinal folds are asymmetric, showing steep northern limbs and, in the region of greatest stress, where the Bath Axis plunges beneath the Mendip Axis, the northern limb is inverted (Fig. 13A). The formation of the periclines was accompanied by isoclinal folding and thrust faulting, some of which is of the nature of drag-faulting.

The next major east-west fold belt north of the Mendips is that which runs through Broadfield Down to Bath, but here the faulting in the Carboniferous

Limestone is less severe. Between these two major fold belts the Coal Measures —two thick groups of incompetent shales separated by a thick mass of sandstone —have been compressed. Relief of stress has been accomplished largely by thrust-faulting, the chief belt of which lies at the centre of the basin in the Farmborough Compression Zone (Figs. 3 and 13A). Here three major thrusts are developed having a total throw of nearly 900 ft. accompanied by a shortening of the beds by nearly $\frac{3}{4}$ mile. Evidence of further relief is seen in the numerous overlap faults developed within the incompetent shales: these faults range from a few feet to those like the ' Radstock Slide ' (Fig. 11) with a maximum horizontal displacement of about 1,500 ft. These thrusts probably resulted

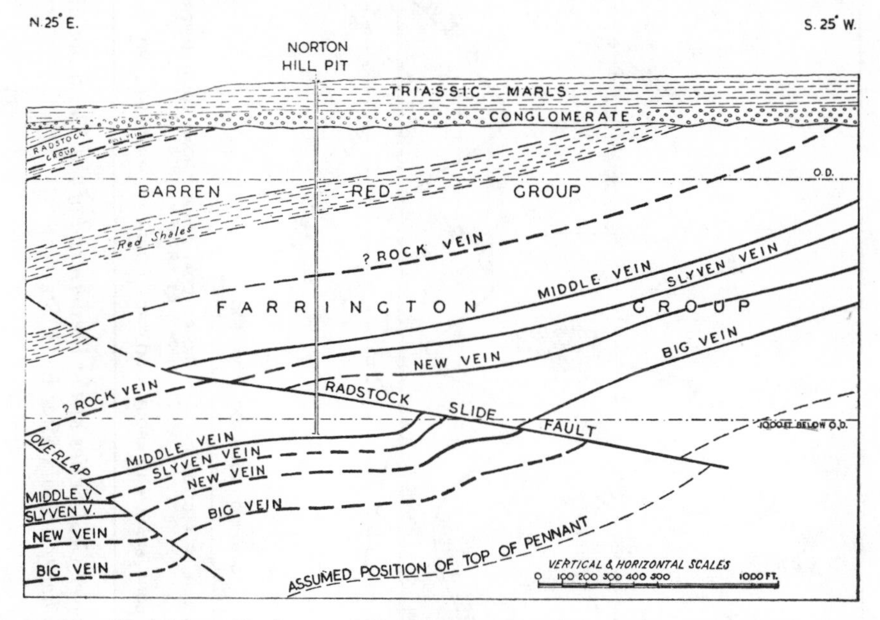

FIG. 11. *Overthrust Faulting. The ' Radstock Slide ' at Norton Hill Colliery, Somerset*

from the squeezing of the soft measures in the major fold and would be expected to flatten out at depth, in which case they would not pass through the Pennant from the Upper to the Lower Coal Series.

Finally, in the Bristol area is developed the remarkable anticlinal structure, known as the Kingswood Anticline (Fig. 12) in which steep disharmonic folding is accompanied by thrust faulting both from north and south. The beds affected are soft sediments of the Lower Coal Series, and it is probable that the underlying Carboniferous Limestone is only gently arched. The Kingswood Anticline thus appears as a gigantic set of wrinkles produced in incompetent strata by two opposing forces: the one being the northward thrusting, the other the resistance to this movement offered by the increasing constriction of the area between the converging Bath and Lower Severn Axes. Along the main axis of the anticline the easiest relief was upwards, and some of the folds are diapiric, i.e., they burst up through the overlying strata.

The east-west folds cross the plunging Lower Severn Axis without much interruption as far north as Clevedon, but farther north, the rising axis appears

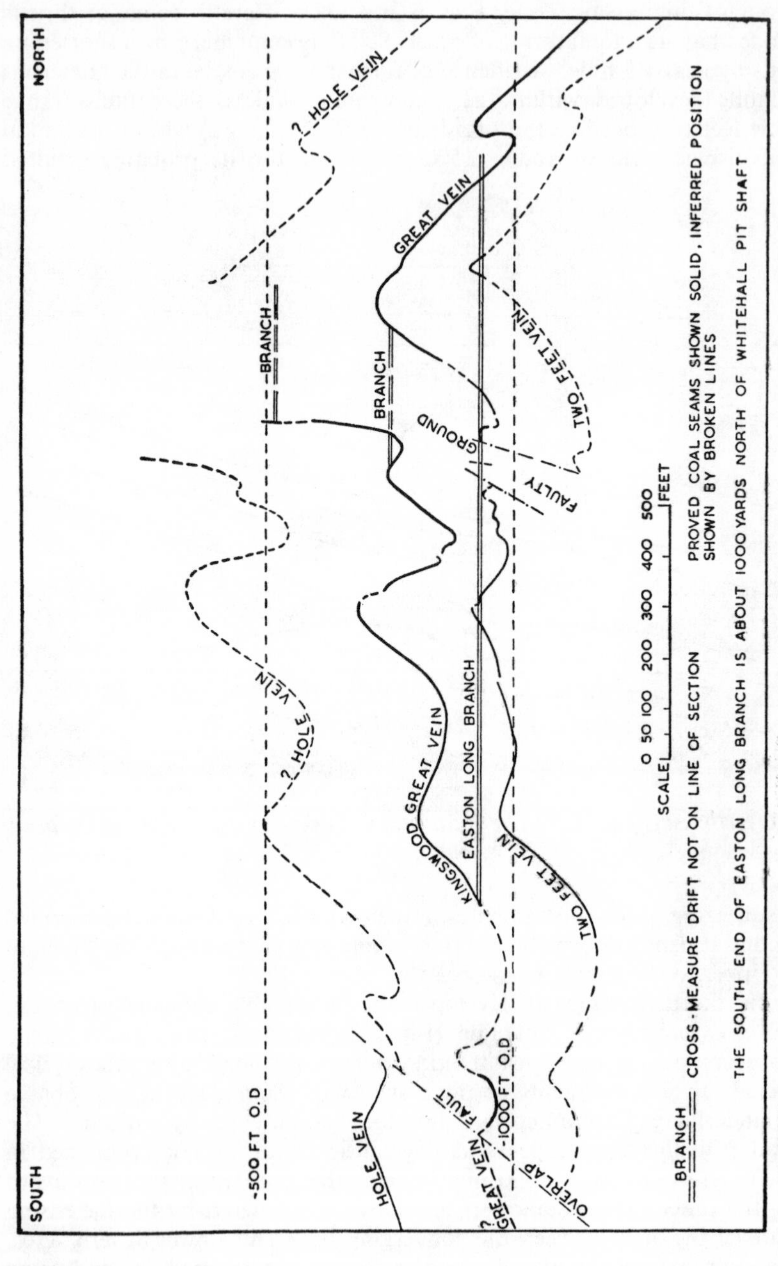

FIG. 12. *Section through part of the Lower Coal Series at the Western end of the Kingswood Anticline, Easton Colliery, Bristol* (After E. H. Staples)

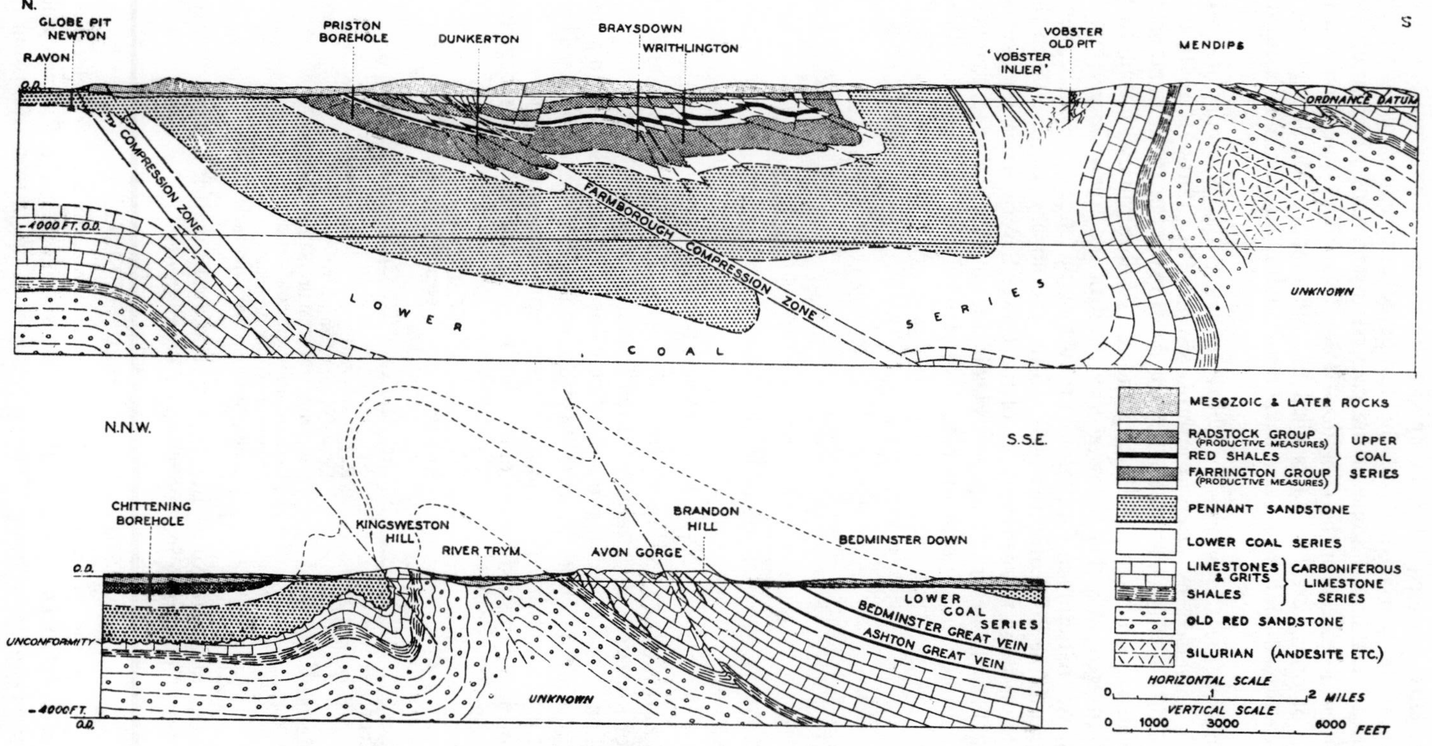

FIG. 13. *Sections to show the suggested structure of parts of the Bristol—Somerset Coalfield*
A. Section from River Avon southwards to the Mendips
B. Section across the Westbury Anticline

to have caused a deflection in the direction of movement from north to north-west. This effect resulted from the application of intense pressure almost at right angles to the earlier folds of the Lower Severn Axis, already a well-defined belt of weakness. Some of the greatest dislocations which affect the strata such as those seen in the Clevedon—Portishead ridge were produced in this way: not only were new folds piled up, but much of the lower Severn Axis was deformed and may even have been slightly displaced in a north-westerly direction.

The whole of the Clevedon—Portishead area and the Westbury-on-Trym Anticline is traversed by steep overthrust faults (Fig. 13B). Here further evidence of intense stresses is afforded by the development of friction and gash-breccias, whilst the rocks show shearing and recrystallization and incompetent strata are squeezed out. The great reversed fault of the Avon Gorge (Fig. 5) and the intense shattering at Cattybrook are further evidence of this movement.

Farther north the dislocation was less violent and appears to have taken the form of folding along the general lines of the Lower Severn Axis: the axes of the new fold lines, however, did not always coincide with the earlier formed ones as is shown by the main north-south folding of the Forest of Dean Coalfield (Fig. 9).

X. TRIAS

(New Red Sandstone)

THE NEW RED SANDSTONE rocks form the lower part of a great series of sediments of Mesozoic age attaining a total thickness of some 3,000 ft. in parts of the Region. These beds have a relatively low dip and rest with marked angular disconformity upon the eroded surface of the Palaeozoic rocks. Their formation therefore clearly post-dates the main Armorican movements.

The following major subdivisions of the New Red Sandstone can be recognized within the region:

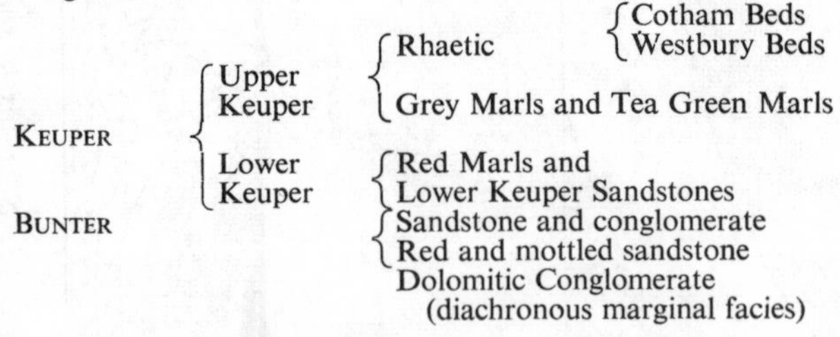

Keuper	Upper Keuper	Rhaetic	Cotham Beds Westbury Beds
		Grey Marls and Tea Green Marls	
	Lower Keuper	Red Marls and Lower Keuper Sandstones	
Bunter		Sandstone and conglomerate Red and mottled sandstone	
		Dolomitic Conglomerate (diachronous marginal facies)	

The rocks grouped above as Bunter are concealed save for a small area in West Somerset. They may include strata of Permian age.

CONDITIONS OF DEPOSITION

The piling up of the Armorican folds was accompanied by a general elevation of the Palaeozoic rocks into a great land mass on which the Permian and Triassic deserts came into being. The early stages in the process of erosion to which the older rocks were subjected cannot be reconstructed, but by Bunter times much of the softer Coal Measures had probably been stripped off the folds to expose the Carboniferous Limestone in the cores, since the Bunter conglomerates when traced from the East Devon coast towards Williton and Puriton are found to contain an increasing quantity of pebbles of grit and Carboniferous Limestone.

In Bunter times the Mendips and the Bristol Coalfield formed a hilly or mountainous tract falling southwards towards a great trough flanking the West Somerset and Devon highlands. In the north a similar basin, lying east of the Malverns and of the Bath Axis extended to the Vale of Moreton Axis. In the deeper parts of these internal basins the detritus from the weathered highlands, either borne by the wind or washed down by torrents, after sudden storms, accumulated in the form of water-laid dust, sand, or pebbles.

By Keuper times a considerable thickness of rock, mostly silty mud and sandstone, had been built up in this way and the concentration or evaporation of saline lakes gave rise to deposits of celestine, gypsum and rock salt collectively known as ' evaporites.' At the same time thick screes of angular rock debris accumulated on the mountain slopes flanking the interior basins. These deposits are well seen in the Bristol and Mendip areas, where they are known as the Dolomitic Conglomerate. Boulders many tons in weight are present where the screes are banked against steep cliffs of Carboniferous Limestone as in the Bridge Valley Road section in the Avon Gorge. Excellent sections showing Dolomitic Conglomerate resting on an eroded surface of Old Red Sandstone may be seen on the coast between Portishead and Clevedon.

Dolomitic Conglomerate overlain by red marl and sandstone was found resting on Carboniferous rocks in the western part of the Severn Tunnel, and is well developed in the Portskewet—Caldicot area. In the country south-west of Chepstow the Dolomitic Conglomerate attains a considerable thickness and also forms the English Stones, Ladybench and other reefs and benches in the Severn Estuary where it rests upon Coal Measures sandstone. Over much of South Monmouthshire, however, the marginal facies is represented by hard, pinkish, impure dolomite.

On the fringes of the Dolomitic Conglomerate fine-grained breccia and dolomite pass into the normal Red Marls and sandstones. Where the breccias, derived from the larger ranges such as the Mendips, pass outwards onto the more deeply eroded surface of the Coal Measures huge spreads of Dolomitic Conglomerate are found at the base of the Red Marls. Thus the Dolomitic Conglomerate extends from the foot of the Mendips northwards for a distance of eight miles across the relatively flat surface of the Coal Measures.

The Dolomitic Conglomerate may pass laterally into rocks varying from Bunter to Upper Keuper in age and is therefore regarded as a diachronous marginal facies.

In the Somerset and Bristol Coalfield the form of the pre-New Red Sandstone surface is of great interest. Where the Red Marls and Dolomitic Conglomerate have been eroded away, the northern face of the Mendips rises at the present day as a great reddened wall of vertical or slightly over-folded and dolomitized limestone at the foot of which the low-lying Coal Measures surface is overlain by an impersistent cover of New Red Sandstone rocks. Similar steep dolomitized faces are found around Broadfield Down and other denuded limestone folds.

Such a surface of uninverted or structural relief would be produced by desert erosion where the limestone cores of the anticlines had been laid bare by the destruction of the Coal Measures. In the absence of a rainfall sufficiently persistent to maintain streams on the limestone areas or to remove the limestone in solution, stream erosion would tend to become concentrated on the softer and less pervious Coal Measures. Similarly, in periods of long drought, wind erosion on the plain would tend to maintain rather than to reduce the slope of the limestone cliffs.

The possibility that the sculpturing of this ancient land-surface was due to desert erosion receives support from the occurrence of well-rounded sand-grains of quartz and fragments of Carboniferous Limestone in the sandstone bands in the Red Marls. Where the Dolomitic Conglomerate is absent and the Red Marls overlie the Coal Measures, a vivid red sandstone commonly forms the base of the New Red Sandstone. The deep red colour of these rocks is due to the presence of thin skins of haematite around the sand grains or to the earthy form of haematite known as red ochre, believed to be derived from the oxidation of pyrite in the Coal Measures shales.

By late Keuper times the accumulation of rock debris on the slopes of the areas of high relief and the deposition of red silt and sand in the interior basins had substantially reduced the surface relief. At the same time the closing phase of deposition of the Red Marls is marked by the presence of an increasing number of green bands which may indicate a gradual amelioration of the climate as humid periods became longer and more frequent.

Thin impersistent layers of gypsum and pseudomorphs of rock salt are found in the green bands at the top of the Red Marls and in the Tea Green Marls which succeeded them, but they become increasingly rare at higher horizons.

Finally the surface subsided beneath the waters of the Rhaetic sea which, though probably landlocked and stagnant, was able to support a limited marine fauna.

The fauna and flora of the New Red Sandstone supports the picture of conditions in Permo-Trias times outlined above. Very few fossils are found in the red rocks apart from the bones of terrestrial reptiles. These include the dinosaurs *Thecodontosaurus* and *Palaeosaurus* found in the Dolomitic Conglomerate of Bristol and the Rhynchocephalian *Glevosaurus hudsoni* recently found near Cromhall.

In the Staunton—Newnham district *Euestheria*, *Hybodus* and plant remains have been recorded from a bed of sandstone in the Red Marls some 215 ft. below the Rhaetic. This bed, known as the Arden Sandstone, was also exposed in the railway-cutting at Ripple near Tewkesbury, where a tooth of *Ceratodus* was found. Such few occurrences tend to emphasize the impression of palaeontological barrenness of the bulk of these rocks, which are normally devoid of organic remains.

The proximity of land in West Somerset during Grey Marl times is indicated by the occurrence near Watchet of a unique tooth of *Hypsiprymnopsis rhaeticus*, the earliest known British mammal. The marine Rhaetic fauna which appears in greater numbers and variety in the overlying black shale consists largely of thin-shelled lamellibranchs which may well have lived in a stagnant sea, while the formation of the succeeding Cotham Beds marked the establishment of a uniformly shallow muddy sea or lagoon only entered by marine organisms at infrequent intervals. Where the mud-flats dried out suncracked layers were formed, while pools of fresh or brackish water were colonized by algae and liverworts, and periodic inroads of the sea led to the formation of thin bands with marine shells.

BUNTER

Bunter Beds have not been seen at the surface but were encountered at depth in a boring at Puriton in Somerset. The lowest strata proved in the borehole consist of 580 ft. of brick-red sandstone with green spots and blotches interbedded with marl or silt. These are overlain by about 100 ft. of pale sandstones with quartz pebbles and a band containing clay pellets and pebbles of Carboniferous Limestone, the whole considered to be of Bunter age.

Bunter rocks probably exist at great depth in the Gloucester district of the Severn Valley, but they are absent in the Bristol and Mendip district of the central part of the region where the Keuper rocks, having overstepped the lower beds, rest directly on Coal Measures or older rocks.

KEUPER

The Keuper has a wide superficial extent beneath the drift-covered plains of Somerset and around the Mendip Hills, and extends northwards through Bristol and Avonmouth along the Severn Valley to Tewkesbury and the Worcestershire border.

Lower Keuper Sandstones.—In Central Somerset and in the Gloucester area of the Severn Valley where the Red Marl and Lower Keuper Sandstone attain their greatest thickness the lower beds consist largely of sandstones. These are 80 to 90 ft. in thickness beneath Puriton, but have been proved to be about 200 ft. thick west of Gloucester. In north Gloucestershire and the Midlands they are known as the ' Waterstones,' from a fancied resemblance to the shading of watered silk, and are exposed in the Newent district where they consist of red and white sandstones intercalated with marl. Eastwards the beds thin out towards the Vale of Moreton Anticline, and were proved to be only 74 ft. thick at Lower Lemington where they rest on Coal Measures, the Bunter having been overstepped in the area to the west.

Red Marls.—The Red Marls which succeeded the Lower Keuper Sandstone have a maximum thickness of at least 1,400 ft. The beds consist largely of red dolomitic silty mud with a starchy or feebly conchoidal fracture and, though slightly calcareous, hardly warrant the use of the term marl which is usually applied to highly calcareous clays like those of the Lias.

The higher parts of this series have veins and mottlings of green, the difference in colour being ascribed to the relative state of oxidation of the iron compounds which give the rock its colour. Thick but impersistent beds of sandstone are developed locally, as in Bristol and parts of South Monmouthshire, and evaporites including celestine, gypsum, rock salt, calcite and small quantities of barytes are also found.

In the immediate vicinity of Bristol the Red Marls may contain masses of coarsely crystalline calcite with small specks of galena and bright green copper minerals, while geodes or hollow nodules lined with rock-crystal or quartz of red, yellow and amethystine hue achieved fame in the past under the exciting name of ' Bristol Diamonds'.

The evaporite deposits are of economic value and of considerable scientific interest. They may include a lower gypsum horizon said to contain traces of strontium and barytes lying about 250 to 500 ft. below the saliferous marls at Puriton, where these salt-bearing marls are thought to be between 700 and 770 ft. below the top of the Red Marls and where they are overlain by red and green variegated marls in which the Upper Gypsum Bed is present.

North of the Mendips in the angle enclosed between the Lower Severn Axis and the Bath Axis, only the upper part of the Red Marls is present, and the Upper Gypsum Bed, with which the celestine deposits are to be correlated, is the only major evaporite deposit to occur. This bed lies at an average depth of 50 to 60 ft. below the top of the Red Marls and is well exposed at Aust Cliff, where the primary deposit consists of large masses of pink and white gypsum. This is accompanied by secondary strings and veins of the fibrous form of hydrated calcium sulphate known as ' Satin Spar.'

In the Yate area both gypsum and celestine occur, the latter having been extensively worked. Celestine is of widespread occurrence at this high horizon and the bed may be traced southwards to the Bitton district where, though thin, it can be identified some 20 to 30 ft. below the junction of the Red and Tea Green Marls. The celestine-rich area lies almost entirely within the arms of the Lower Severn and Bath axes, extending over the Tytherington district and southwards to Bristol and the flanks of the Mendips. Celestine has also been observed in some quantity in the marginal Keuper rocks of the Westbury (Somerset) area south of the Mendips; but still within the limits set by the ancient axes.

The most concentrated deposits are to be found in the north of this inter-axial region, and the fact that celestine does not occur to any great extent in the Newark Gypsum Lake of the Midlands suggests that there was no direct connection with this inland basin to the north.

Tea Green and Grey Marls.—The most complete succession of Upper Keuper rocks is exposed in the coastal sections of West Somerset, where there is a transition from the Red Marls to calcareous green clays and mudstones known as the Tea Green Marls, which in turn pass upwards into the Grey Marls. The Tea Green and Grey Marls reach a total thickness of 110 ft. at Blue Anchor, and the presence of the Rhaetic lamellibranch *Pteria contorta* in the upper part of the Grey Marls at Lilstock shows that the stratigraphical break between the Tea Green Marls and the Rhaetic is much smaller than is found farther north.

On being traced northwards the Grey Marls become less prominent, being represented at Uphill by 7 ft. of calcareous mudstone interbedded with dark grey or black shale; here, too, the Tea Green Marls are reduced to 33 ft. of clay and mudstone with traces of gypsum.

Northwards towards Bristol the Tea Green Marls diminish to an average thickness of 15 ft. and in the Keynsham district contain slight traces of the dark shale bands which characterize the Grey Marls of Uphill and West Somerset. These are found as wisps or lenticles in a median nodular band of brecciated, silty, calcareous mudstone lying within the local Tea Green Marls. Beyond the Bristol Avon the Grey Marls have not yet been recorded, and at Aust Cliff (Pl. VII) and other sections along the banks of the River Severn the Tea Green Marls are more clearly differentiated from the Red Marls below and the black shales above than they are in the splendid cliff sections of West Somerset.

Rhaetic.—Reference has already been made to the occurrence of Rhaetic fossils including *Pteria contorta* in the top of the Grey Marls of West Somerset. The non-sequence between the Westbury Beds and the Grey Marls therefore lies above the point at which Rhaetic fossils first appear in this area. Elsewhere in the region the first marine Rhaetic fossils are found in the Westbury Beds and for all practical purposes the base of the Rhaetic may be taken as coincident with the bottom of the black shales. The upper limit of the Rhaetic is taken at the Cotham Marble lying at the junction of the Cotham Beds and the White Lias.

Westbury Beds.—The Westbury Beds take their name from Garden Cliff, Westbury-on-Severn, where the beds are well exposed. They are better developed at Blue Anchor in Somerset where they reach their maximum thickness of about 45 ft. Here the Tea Green and Grey Marls are succeeded by black shale with thin beds of limestone and sandstone. The junction of the Westbury Beds with the underlying Green and Grey Marls is always non-sequential, though the angular disconformity may be so slight as to be unnoticeable. The sudden change from grey or green to black and the presence of fragments or pebbles of the underlying rocks in the base of the Westbury Beds shows, however, that the former suffered erosion prior to the deposition of the black shale.

Thin-shelled lamellibranchs are quite abundant in some bands of the black shales and include *Pteria contorta*, '*Schizodus*' *ewaldi*, *Chlamys valoniensis*, and *Palaeocardita cloacina*, small gastropods, fish remains and other fossils. Thin limestones full of *Chlamys valoniensis*, *Placunopsis alpina* and other forms can be traced locally, and form useful but limited aids to correlation. In this respect the most interesting and reliable bed is the Ceratodus Bone Bed, a conglomeratic sandy limestone which passes locally into ginger-coloured sandstone. As the name suggests, the rock is packed with vertebrate remains, mainly the scales, teeth and spines of *Acrodus*, *Hybodus*, *Gyrolepis* and other fishes, together with the bones and teeth of saurians such as *Ichthyosaurus* and *Plesiosaurus*. The most characteristic remains are the palatal teeth of *Ceratodus* —a relative of the modern Australian lung-fish—and the Ceratodus Bone Bed is distinguished from other minor occurrences of vertebrate remains by its presence.

At Blue Anchor in West Somerset, the Ceratodus Bone Bed lies some 20 ft. above the base of the Westbury Beds and the underlying shales yield *Pteromya crowcombeia* and *Pteria contorta*.

Shales occur beneath the Bone Bed in Central Somerset and at Uphill, but north of the Mendips the Bone Bed is usually found resting on the Tea Green Marl, as at Aust, or on older rocks as at Chipping Sodbury (*see* Fig. 14) and in the Eastern Mendips. Even the Bone Bed is missing at many localities in the Bristol area where the higher parts of the Westbury Beds may rest unconformably on the Palaeozoic rocks.

The erosion which preceded the deposition of the Westbury Beds in the Mendip area and the country to the north was of a much more severe nature than that which took place in the south. The widespread submergence that followed it, and which may be called the Rhaetic Transgression, led to the deposition of fine black muds on an eroded surface composed of a wide variety of formations. Fragments of Tea Green and Red Marl, and insoluble residues such as rolled phosphate pellets and quartz pebbles are abundant in the basal Bone Bed or, where this is missing, may be seen lying on the eroded surface beneath the black shales.

There are no such extensive deposits of littoral Rhaetic as are found in Glamorgan, but at Butcombe, north of the Mendips, the rocks pass into a conglomerate packed with well-rounded pebbles of Carboniferous Limestone. A Mendip shore-line may have contributed to this deposit, and the occurrence of the Rhaetic mammal *Microcleptes moorei*, found in fissures in the Carboniferous Limestone at Holwell near Frome, proves the existence of one or more Mendip islands at this time.

In general the changes in thickness of the Westbury Beds may be ascribed to the overlapping of the lower horizons against irregularities on an eroded

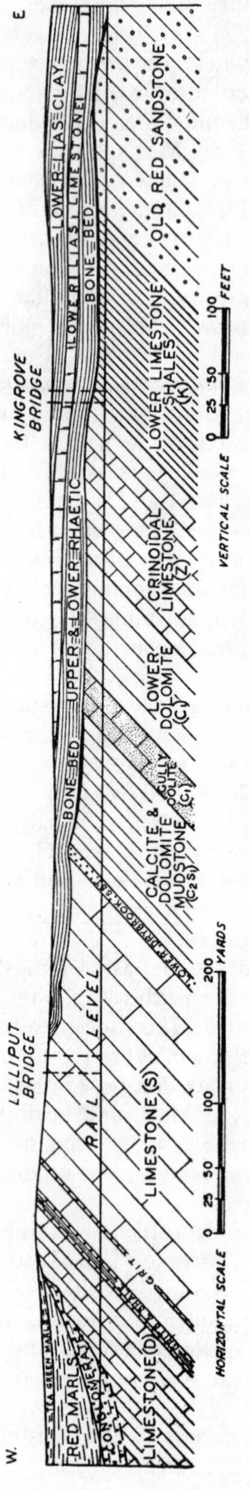

FIG. 14. *Section of railway cutting south of Chipping Sodbury, Gloucestershire*

floor of older rocks; where the undulations were produced entirely by localized scouring or were modified by slight folding before deposition was resumed remains to be determined.

Cotham Beds.—A non-sequence marks the junction of the Westbury and the overlying Cotham Beds. The latter consist of soft greenish-grey silty calcite mud, at the top of which lies the well-known Cotham Marble. The total thickness of the Cotham Beds is rarely more than 5 or 6 ft. and they include no deposits of known economic value. The location of the Cotham Beds and to some extent of the Westbury Beds also is, however, of importance to the engineer since these rocks have low bearing strength particularly when in a weathered condition.

The fauna of the Cotham Beds is impoverished and stunted, and in West and Central Somerset very few fossils are to be found. North of the Mendips they are slightly less barren and a thin bed of banded calcite mudstone in the lower part of the Cotham Beds has both plant and shell-bearing layers. In the Naiadites Bed, as this is called, the freshwater and brackish layers yield the liverworts *Naiadites lanceolata* and *Hepaticites*, together with algae, insect larvae and occasional specimens of the phyllopod *Euestheria minuta*.

Euestheria is more often found in the mudstone layers between the plant-bearing and marine layers. The layers with *Euestheria*, and the marine and plant-bearing horizons are usually distinct from one another, but an occasional fish scale or *Euestheria* may be found in the plant-bearing layers. Thin beds showing sun-cracks and, more rarely, ripple-marks and worm-tracks, also occur in the Naiadites Bed.

The fauna of the marine bands yields *Chlamys valoniensis* and other lamellibranchs found in the Westbury Beds below.

The Cotham Marble takes its name from the type locality of Cotham, Bristol. It is a hard splintery calcite-mudstone with an irregular top and a flat smooth base. In Gloucestershire it passes locally into a hard fissile limestone with *Pseudomonotis fallax*, but elsewhere fossils, apart from fish scales, are rare. The bed is seldom more than 6 to 8 in. thick and is notable for the tree-like markings seen when the rock is broken in a vertical plane; hence the popular name 'Landscape Marble.' In the past it was used as an ornamental stone, both cut and polished for indoor use and employed outside for walls and ornamental rockeries.

The basal layers of the Cotham Marble show flinty-looking calcite mudstone with distorted or undulating surfaces and small-scale slump-structures in some localities. The origin of the internal tree-like markings has usually been ascribed to the upward movement of bubbles of dark oily mud moving slowly through unconsolidated calcite mud and stimulated by slumping movements in the basal layers. Recently it has been claimed that the 'landscape' is an association of algal growths occurring in convex masses. Other types known as 'False' or 'Crazy' Cotham Marble have been formed by the penecontemporaneous breaking up of partly consolidated calcite mud.

XI. LIAS

IT HAS ALREADY been seen that towards the end of Triassic times, intermittent incursions of the sea into the area of the deserts and their inland basins, led to the deposition of marine strata of Rhaetic age. This phase heralded a great change in physical conditions which was completed at an early stage of the Jurassic Period by the deposition of the purely marine Liassic rocks.

The major subdivisions of the Lias, with approximate thicknesses in feet, are as follows:

	South of Bath		*North of Bath*	
UPPER LIAS			Scissum Bed	0–30
			Cephalopod Bed	0–20
	Midford and Yeovil Sands	0–215	Cotteswold Sands	0–230
			Upper Lias Clay	0–270
UPPER AND MIDDLE LIAS	Junction Bed	0–25		
MIDDLE LIAS	Pennard Sands	0–80	Marlstone Rock Bed	0–15
	Middle Lias Marls	0–100	Middle Lias Marls	0–250
LOWER LIAS	Lower Lias Clay } up to	600	Lower Lias Clay	100–960
	Blue Lias Limestone } up to		Blue Lias Limestone	10–30
	White Lias	0–20	White Lias	0–12

LOWER LIAS

DEPOSITIONAL HISTORY

The depositional history of the Lias, like that of the earlier formations, has been profoundly affected by earth movements along structural axes. Many of these movements are said to be ' posthumous ': that is to say, they have taken place at intervals along pre-existing fold lines or belts of weakness.

Both the Severn and Bath axes, and the younger Armorican folds, have in this way influenced the form of the basins in which the Lias was deposited, and thus have controlled the distribution of the varied sediments which compose this formation.

We may consider first the form of the basin of deposition in which the White Lias was laid down (Fig. 15). This shows the influence of both the Lower Severn and the Bath axes. The position of the Lower Severn Axis is clearly indicated by the extreme thinness or absence of the White Lias in its vicinity. It will be noted, however, that the Mendip Axis had less effect on the general shape of the basin, although the normal sediments pass into a massive littoral facies near the old shore-line.

It is probable that the White Lias was formed in a large lagoon or partly land-locked sea where subsidence was insufficient to keep pace with deposition.

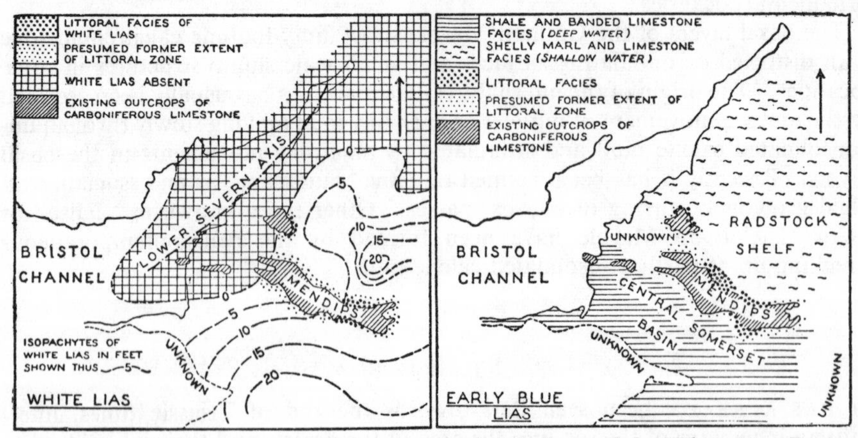

FIG. 15.—*Sketch-maps showing* A.—*Probable form of the White Lias Basin*
B.—*The two facies of the basal Blue Lias*

The lagoon thus became filled with deposits which thin out towards the margin of the basin and successively overlap the earlier formed strata. Thus the topmost bed, a hard white calcite-mudstone known as the ' Sun Bed ' or ' Jew Stone', has a greater lateral extension than the beds underneath.

Towards the close of White Lias times the turbid and shallowing water became inimical to marine life, and drained away or dried up as the result of a gentle elevation of the whole region. Ensuing slight erosion of the ' Sun Bed ' was followed by a widespread submergence (in which parts of the Mendips did not share) and by the deposition of the Blue Lias.

THE AMMONITE ZONES OF THE LIAS

UPPER LIAS	*Lioceras opalinum**
	Lytoceras jurense
	Hildoceras bifrons
	Hildoceras serpentinum
	Dactylioceras tenuicostatum
MIDDLE LIAS	*Pleuroceras spinatum*
	Amaltheus margaritatus
LOWER LIAS	*Prodactylioceras davoei*
	Tragophylloceras ibex
	Uptonia jamesoni
	Echioceras raricostatum
	Oxynoticeras oxynotum
	Asteroceras obtusum
	Arietites turneri
	Arnioceras semicostatum
	Ammonites bucklandi
	Scamnoceras angulatum
	Psiloceras planorbis

* This zone is here grouped with the Lias rather than with the Inferior Oolite for convenience of description, a practice adopted by W. J. Arkell in *The Jurassic System in Britain*, 1933.

The initial phase of the deposition of the Blue Lias was characterized by the formation of thin bedded grey limestones with partings of shale and marl. These are often referred to as the *Ostrea* limestones, and unlike the succeeding beds, do not contain ammonites.

The appearance of the ammonite *Psiloceras* in the strata above the *Ostrea* limestones is not accompanied by any appreciable change in lithology over most of the region. Yet it marks the establishment of a connection with a Mediterranean sea known as the Tethys from which the British area had been separated throughout Permian and Triassic times. From this period onwards successive waves of ammonites entered the Lias seas in large numbers, and spread rapidly over wide areas. Some families survived longer than others, but all include a variety of species, many combining a short vertical range with wide distribution; features which make them ideal zonal fossils.

The ammonite zones and subzones (*see* table above) have proved to be of great value both in the demonstration of non-sequences and in showing how conditions of deposition varied from place to place at any given period.

As an example of a non-sequence we may take the case of the Oxynotum Zone. Reference to Fig. 16 shows that this zone, characterized by *Oxynoticeras* and *Bifericeras*, is present in the Lower Lias clays south of the Mendips, but on the north side of the axis it is usually absent, that is to say there is a non-sequence between the Raricostatum Zone and the Obtusum Zone. Such a non-sequence marks the incidence of a period of slight uplift of the sea floor which has caused non-accumulation of sediment or removal of deposits previously formed.

The second use to which the ammonite zones can be put is in the demonstration of contemporaneous variation in conditions of sedimentation. This is well illustrated by the changes in the lithology of the Bucklandi Zone (Fig. 16).

It will be recalled that in White Lias times the form of the basin of deposition was determined largely by movement of the Lower Severn and Bath axes. Early in Blue Lias times, however, the form of the basin underwent a profound change. The effect of this can be best understood by considering the distribution of the two facies of the basal Blue Lias limestones and comparing the form of the early Blue Lias sea with that of the White Lias. (*See* Fig. 15.)

Some of the lateral changes which may be observed in the Blue Lias rocks are described below. When considered in relation to the position of the ancient axes of folding, these lithological variations are seen to be of considerable significance.

There is no evidence that the Lower Severn Axis played more than a minor part in determining the form of the early Blue Lias seas. On the other hand, the Mendips now appear as the dividing line between two distinct facies.

Thus to the south of the Mendips the *Ostrea* limestones and the two subzones of the Planorbis Zone (planorbis and johnstoni subzones) form a virtually continuous series of thin limestones and clays. At the same time the perfectly preserved vertebrate remains found in the rocks show that the bones were not scattered after decay of the soft tissues, but were buried where they lay by the accumulation of fine mud settling through calm water. Here the sea bed must have lain below the zone of wave and current action.

North of the Mendips different conditions prevailed. In contrast with the deposits south of the Mendips the comparable beds in South Gloucestershire and North Somerset are nearly all coarse shelly limestones and marls. Vertebrate remains, when found, are usually in the form of isolated bones and teeth. Furthermore, the stratigraphical succession is often incomplete, the planorbis subzone being absent locally while the johnstoni subzone is often greatly condensed.

In the earliest Blue Lias deposits this shallow-water facies is found to extend as far to the north as the Dursley area where the outcrop of the Lower Lias crosses the Bath Axis. North and east of the axis conditions tend to parallel those of the deeper water facies of the Central Somerset basin.

The rocks composing the later zones of the Lower Lias show, however, that as time went on the area covered by the shallows gradually shrank as the water deepened in the north. Thus by the time the Bucklandi Zone was deposited, the shelly limestone facies was restricted to a district lying south of a line drawn approximately from Filton to Wick.

Around Radstock, however, folding and elevation of the sea-bed maintained the belt of shallow water for a much longer period. Here shelly, phosphatic, and ferruginous limestones were laid down until late in Lower Lias times. The intra-Liassic fold lines determined by J. W. Tutcher and A. E. Trueman are parallel to the main Armorican folds of the Mendips and their direction is therefore thought to have been influenced by the orientation of pre-existing structures in the Palaeozoic rocks beneath. No direct relationship between individual Jurassic and Armorican folds is implied in this case and the term 'posthumous movement' which is sometimes applied to these structures should only be used in a general sense.

As might be expected, there is an intimate connection between sedimentation and the movements in the underlying Palaeozoic rocks. Apart from numerous

(A 6673)

A.—Cannop Colliery, Forest of Dean

(A 6299)

B.—Tyning Batch near Radstock, Somerset

COALFIELD SCENERY

(A 6273)

AUST CLIFF

non-sequences within the Lias, the rich ammonite faunas of the Radstock Shelf show upon analysis that many beds are condensed deposits. These, though they may be only a few inches thick, include fossils which are distributed through tens or even hundreds of feet in the thick clays of Central Somerset or North Gloucestershire.

Nevertheless the stratigraphical order in which the fossils occur is fundamentally the same as that found elsewhere. Where the ammonites of two or more subzones occur together in one bed they are usually in a rolled or phosphatized condition and have clearly been derived from some previously existing deposit which has suffered intraformational erosion.

Separating the Radstock shallows from the Central Somerset basin lay the Mendip littoral. Attempts have been made to reconstruct the fringes of islands which are thought to have composed an archipelago, around which the littoral zone was formed in the Mendips and Broadfield Down, but their form at any given time is still largely a matter of conjecture. Evidence of the existence of one or more islands during part of Lower Lias times is provided by the recent discovery of the remains of a mammal-like reptile (*Oligokyphus*) associated with Lias fossils in a fissure in the Carboniferous Limestone of the Eastern Mendips.

Little is known of the nature of the land flora of the Mendip islands. Fronds of the Cycad, *Otozamites obtusus*, have been found in the White Lias of the Radstock district, but conditions in the more open waters of the Blue Lias seas were even less favourable to preservation, and plant-remains are usually represented only by pieces of fossil drift wood.

The history of Lower Lias times may therefore be summarized as a period in which a thick deposit of marine clays was laid down in the deeper basins of Central Somerset and North Gloucestershire. Movements of the Mendip and, to a lesser extent, of the Bath Axis, gave rise to the Radstock shallows and the Mendip littoral with their associated sediments. The gradual diminution of these movements and a general lowering of the sea floor led to the establishment of more uniform conditions by Davoei Zone times.

GENERAL DESCRIPTION

White Lias.—At Radstock and in Central Somerset, where it has been much quarried for lime and building stone, the White Lias attains a thickness of about 20 ft. It consists of a series of white or pale grey fine-grained limestones and calcite-mudstones, becoming marly and fossiliferous at the base.

The fossils consist dominantly of lamellibranchs, some like *Modiolus* and *Protocardia* being common to the Rhaetic, while others, e.g., *Lima*, *Pleuromya* and *Pholadomya* appear for the first time in the White Lias and are exceedingly abundant in the succeeding strata.

In those areas where the White Lias is absent the overlying Blue Lias rests non-sequentially upon the Rhaetic, but the surface of the latter is seldom found to be deeply eroded.

Blue Lias Limestone and Lower Lias Clay.—Immediately north of the Mendips and in South Gloucestershire the basal beds of the Blue Lias are shallow-water shelly limestones containing abundant *Ostrea*, *Pleuromya* and other lamellibranchs. The beds are well seen in the cliff sections at Aust and Westbury-on-Severn, where they rest upon the Rhaetic. In this area they are seldom more than 5 ft. thick, but farther north thicken to nearly double this amount and in the Tewkesbury district include banded limestones with the remains of insects and crustaceans.

A similar thickening of the *Ostrea* limestones can be seen south of the Mendips, where the beds are less shelly than in the Radstock and Bristol areas and, at Street, have yielded almost perfect skeletons of the great marine saurians *Ichthyosaurus* and *Plesiosaurus*, together with *Pholidophorus*, *Dapedius* and other fishes.

Above the basal limestones in Central Somerset and the Vale of Gloucester the bulk of the Lower Lias consists of clay and shale, but in North Somerset limestones are developed at higher horizons and the total thickness of Blue Lias Limestone including thin clay bands may be up to 50 ft. At Keynsham these include the massive limestones of the Bucklandi Zone with large ammonites such as *Ammonites bucklandi*, and a basal bed rich in *Calcirhynchia*.

The higher zones are better seen at Radstock, where the Bucklandi Bed is overlain by the famous *Spiriferina* Bed, only one or two inches thick, but full of *Spiriferina walcotti*, *Gryphaea*, and other fossils. All the succeeding zones up to the Ibex Zone are thin but they have yielded an important series of ammonites of which the Echiocerates of the Raricostatum Zone are perhaps the most striking group.

In the Eastern Mendips and Broadfield Down the lower zones of the Lias are found to pass into massive shelly and conglomeratic rocks, obviously deposited close inshore. These rocks have been worked for building stone near Shepton Mallet under the name of ' Downside Stone'.

The shelly limestones and phosphatic rocks of Radstock and Keynsham pass northwards into clay and shale with occasional bands of nodular cement-stone (*see* Fig. 16). At Sodbury the Lower Lias attains a thickness of 200 ft. and includes only a small proportion of limestone. This northward thickening is not uniformly maintained into the Vale of Gloucester, for the beds appear to thin over the Bath Axis and then thicken once more to the east of it.

In the Vale of Gloucester the absence of continuous sections suitable for detailed collecting makes it difficult to apportion the thicknesses of individual zones within the main mass of the Lower Lias clays. For the most part the outcrop gives rise to flat or slightly undulating land bounded on the east by the higher ground formed by the Middle Lias and on the west by the River Severn. Such evidence as is available suggests that the clays are very thick, probably more than 500 ft. at Gloucester, and that all the main zones, including the Oxynotum Zone, are present.

The upper part of the Lower Lias clay has been worked for brick, tile, and pipe-making at Stonehouse, Robins Wood Hill, and also at Cheltenham, where at Battledown brickworks the clays of the Ibex and Jamesoni Zones yield well-preserved ammonites including *Tragophylloceras ibex* and *Acanthopleuroceras valdani*.

Above the Jamesoni Zone, the Davoei Zone is characterized by the presence of numerous ' capricorn ' ammonites of which *Androgynoceras maculatum* is an example. The Davoei Zone is, however, more uniform in its lithology than any of the lower zones, being represented by thick clay over most of the region.

North and east of the Cheltenham District, in the vicinity of Mickleton, the Lower Lias is said to attain its maximum thickness of about 960 ft.

Changes in lithology somewhat similar to those which occur when the zones of the Lower Lias are traced northwards can also be demonstrated in the beds extending southwards from the Mendips. Here the transition to clay

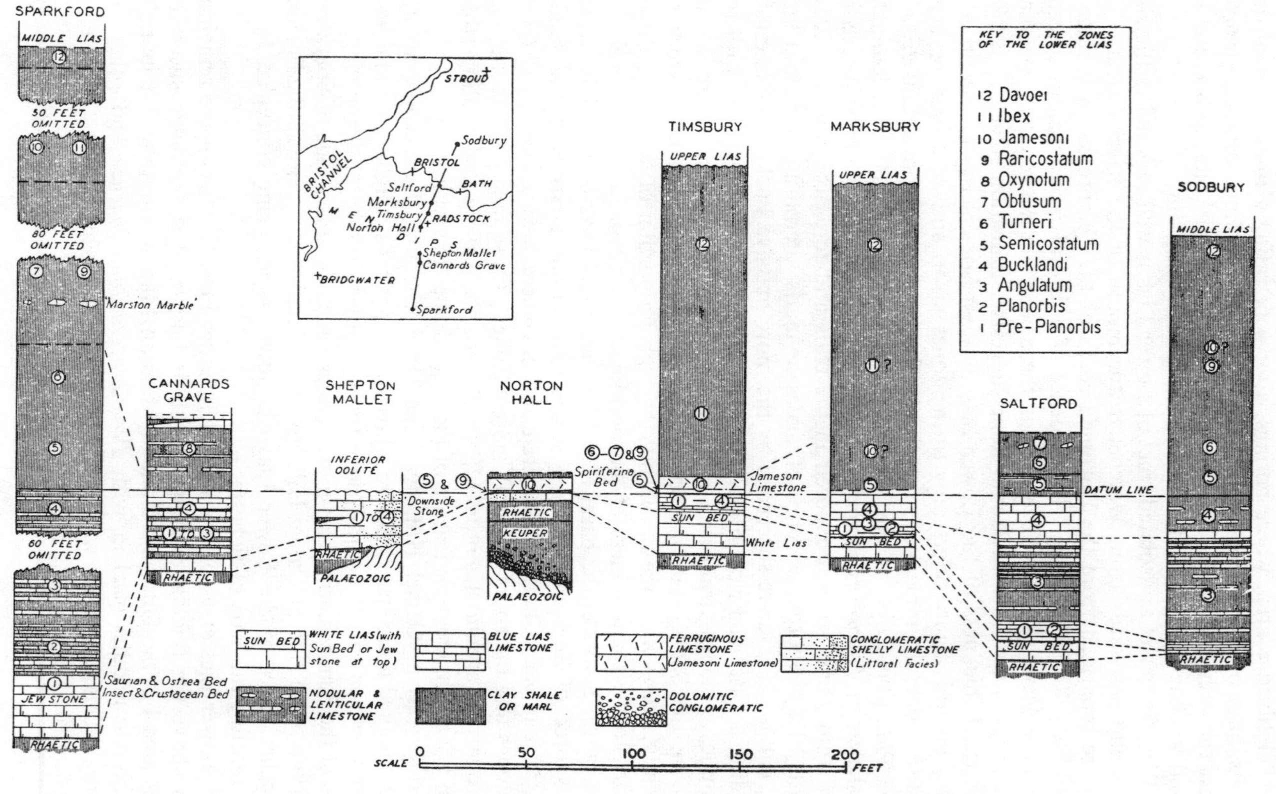

FIG. 16. *Comparative vertical sections of the Lower Lias*

and shale takes place more quickly and there is no wide belt of shallow-water deposits comparable with those of the Radstock Shelf.

The deepest part of the southern basin of deposition is thought to have lain in the Highbridge area, where borings, after penetrating a thick cover of drift deposits, have proved up to 400 ft. of clay. Fossils including *Spiriferina walcotti* suggest the presence of the Bucklandi Zone near the sub-drift surface and the original thickness may therefore have been greater than this.

In West Somerset an isolated tract of Lower Lias is well exposed in the cliffs that extend eastwards from Watchet to the mouth of the River Parret. The rocks are separated from the Devonian rocks of the Quantocks by a tract of faulted New Red Sandstone. No evidence of a littoral facies such as is found around the Mendips has yet been seen in these beds, but the general appearance of the limestones of the Bucklandi Zone suggests a transition stage.

The total thickness of the Lower Lias in West Somerset is of the order of 150 ft., but this figure refers only to the zones up to and including the Semicostatum Zone, the remaining zones having been removed by post-Lias erosion.

The Planorbis Zone of the Watchet area is noted for its finely-laminated blue shale with *Psiloceras planorbis* and *Caloceras johnstoni*, while the succeeding Angulatum Zone, so well exposed in the cliffs and foreshore north of Kilve, consists of a monotonous series of shales or marls alternating with thin limestone bands. These are succeeded by the more massive Bucklandi Limestone, including a basal bed rich in *Calcirhynchia*. Dark bituminous shale with thin limestones yielding *Arnioceras* completes the known succession up to and including the Semicostatum Zone. Attempts have been made to work the shale at Kilve as a source of oil, but the high proportion of sulphur is said to have led to the abandonment of the workings.

In Central Somerset the basal Blue Lias limestones have been widely worked as a source of lime and building stone. Numerous quarries in the Polden Hills, at Dunball, Charlton Mackrell and elsewhere have exposed the *Ostrea* limestones and the rocks of the Planorbis Zone. These flaggy limestones have been quarried around Keinton Mandeville for the paving and walling stones which are a characteristic feature of the local domestic architecture.

Farther east at Camel Hill, near Sparkford, the Blue Lias crops out in a narrow faulted anticlinal structure whose long axis runs roughly east and west. To the north of this structural ridge the Blue Lias dips beneath the clays and shales of the Semicostatum and higher zones which form the Vale of Sparkford.

On the south side of Camel Hill, however, Triassic rocks are faulted against the higher zones of the Lower Lias, the lower zones being concealed by the clays forming the Vale of Ilchester.

The Lower Lias clays of the Vale of Ilchester include most of the remaining zones above the Bucklandi Zone. Little is known of the detailed succession in this area but the Obtusum Zone at Marston Magna is notable for its richly fossiliferous nodules packed with *Promicroceras marstonense* and other ammonites. This limestone was formerly cut and polished under the name of ' Marston Marble '.

Middle Lias

In the Eastern Mendips and the Radstock district the Lower Lias is overlain non-sequentially by Upper Lias or Inferior Oolite rocks and, with the exception of one small patch of Marlstone Rock Bed preserved beneath the Upper Lias

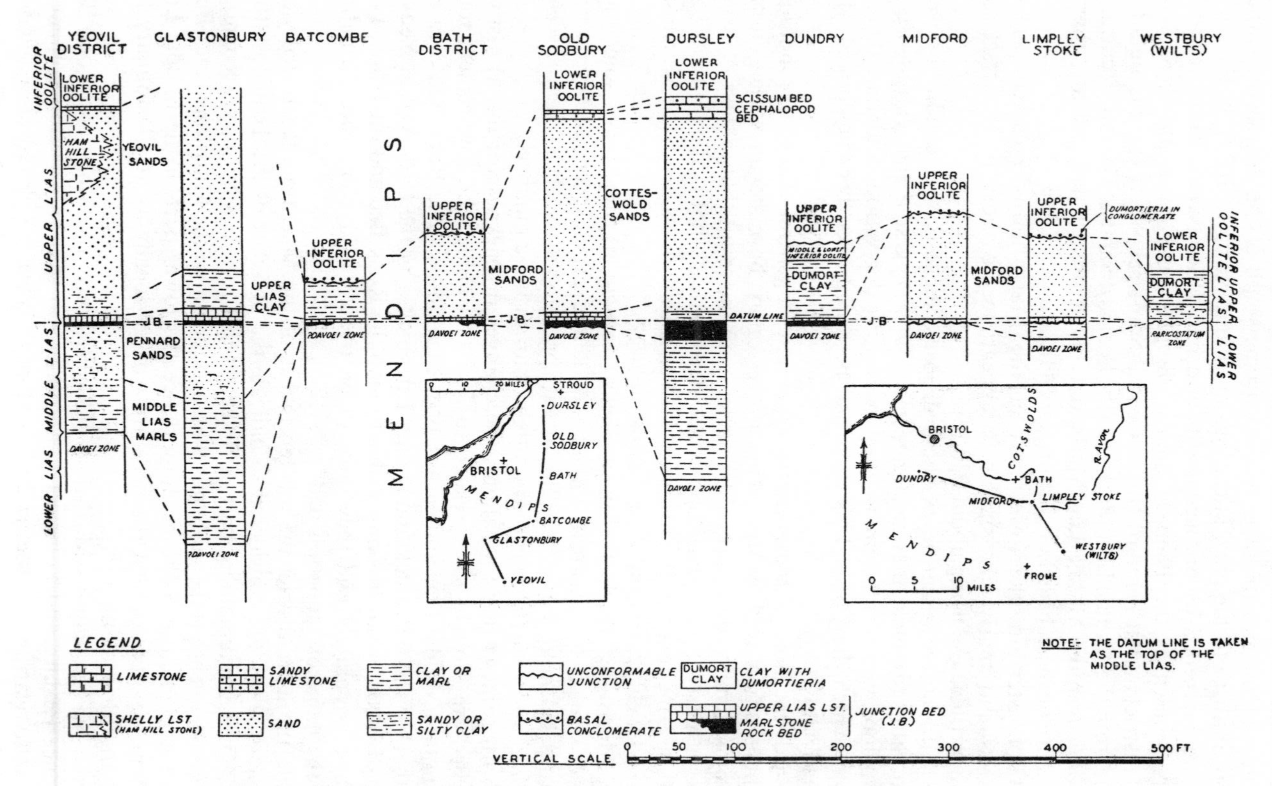

FIG. 17. *Comparative vertical sections of the Middle and Upper Lias*

of Dundry Hill, no Middle Lias is seen in North Somerset. Strata of Middle Lias age are present, however, in Gloucestershire and in the country south of the Mendips, the Lower Lias being succeeded in both cases by marly or sandy micaceous silts in which fossils are very rare.

Around Chard and Ilminster in the extreme south of the district the earliest deposits consist of blue-grey, micaceous marl and silt up to 100 ft. in thickness. These are succeeded by micaceous silts and fine yellow sands, with occasional doggers, known as the Pennard Sands. Similar sandy beds are seen in the Yeovil district and at Pennard Hill in Central Somerset, where there is a gradual passage from the Middle Lias Marls into the Pennard Sands. The rare occurrence of *Amaltheus* in the Middle Lias Marls, notably at Brent Knoll indicates that at least a part of these beds falls within the Margaritatus Zone.

In Gloucestershire the lower part of the Margaritatus Zone consists of micaceous and marly silts similar in appearance to those of Somerset, the maximum thickness being about 230 ft.

The unfossiliferous nature of these deposits suggests that conditions were unfavourable for most marine organisms. It is suggested that subsidence of the sea floor was insufficient to keep pace with deposition, and that the old basins in which the Lower Lias clays had been deposited became choked with sand and silt.

Towards the close of Margaritatus Zone times a general change in conditions of sedimentation took place. This process may have begun earlier in the Cotswolds than in some parts of Somerset, with the result that in the Cotswolds the lower part of the Marlstone Rock Bed contains both Margaritatus and Spinatum Zone fossils. In most of Somerset, on the other hand, the Marlstone Rock Bed yields Spinatum Zone fossils only.

The Marlstone Rock Bed is a shelly ferruginous limestone, sometimes oolitic or sandy. Fossils are abundant and include several species of *Pleuroceras*, numerous belemnites and lamellibranchs; brachiopods such as *Tetrarhynchia tetrahedra* and *Lobothyris punctata* often occur in large numbers.

As with some earlier formations, the changes in thickness of the Marlstone Rock Bed are thought to be related to fold axes along which movement took place in late Middle Lias and early Upper Lias times. The Rock Bed is rarely more than 15 to 20 ft. thick and is only 1 ft. thick over the Bath Axis at Yeovil. Under such conditions it is impossible to map the Rock Bed and the Upper Lias limestones separately and they have to be treated as a composite formation under the name of ' Junction Bed '.

In the Ilminster district the top ten inches of the Marlstone Rock Bed yield ammonites which are considered to indicate the presence of the Tenuicostatum Zone. Over the remaining part of Somerset this zone has not been recognized and a non-sequence is therefore postulated at the top of the Marlstone Rock Bed.

Since it is of little economic importance the lower part of the Middle Lias is seldom exposed, though the beds are worked locally as at Glastonbury for brick- and tile-making.

Unlike the ferruginous Marlstone of Oxfordshire, the Marlstone Rock Bed of Gloucestershire and Somerset is normally too thin and its iron content is too low to warrant its use as an ironstone. When employed as a building stone it has a pleasant colour but is rather soft and there is much waste in quarrying.

Owing to their relative hardness in comparison with the soft sands and clays above and below, the Marlstone Rock Bed and the Junction Bed give rise to characteristic platforms both in Somerset and in the Cotswolds. The Junction Bed platform is well-marked around Ilminster and Corton Denham in Somerset, and is particularly well seen in the outlier of Brent Knoll.

In Gloucestershire the Marlstone Rock Bed forms the conspicuous ledge below the Cotswold scarp—a feature which is well exhibited near Wotton-under-Edge and Stinchcombe (Pl. VIII and Fig. 18)—and gives rise to the flat-topped hills of Diston and Dumbleton and the ledges on Oxenton and Alderton Hills, between Cheltenham and Broadway.

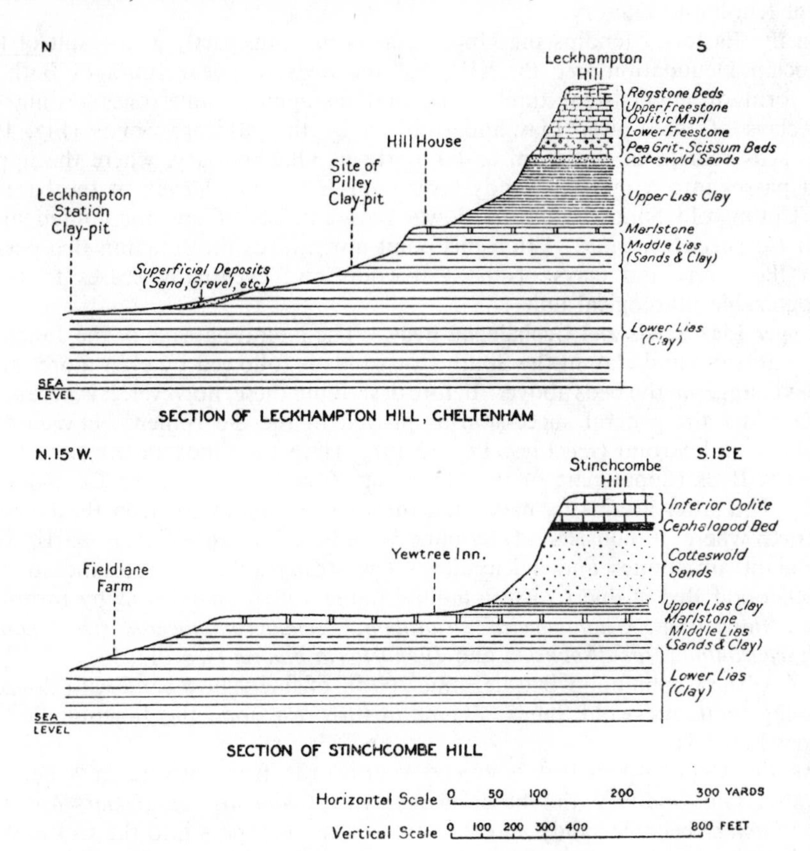

FIG. 18. *Sections across the Cotswold Scarp* (From L. Richardson, *Proc. Cotteswold Nat. Field Club*, vol. xvi, 1908)

UPPER LIAS

Saurian and Fish Beds.—These, the earliest deposits of the Upper Lias in the Bristol and Gloucester district, are found at Ilminster and in the Mid Cotswolds. At Dumbleton they are represented by some 20 ft. of shale with banded limestone nodules yielding fish and insect remains and, like the comparable beds at Ilminster, are thought to lie partly within the Tenuicostatum Zone.

The localized distribution of these beds in the Cotswolds may be due to movement along the axes of the Painswick and Cleeve Hill synclines (*see* Fig. 20) prior to the deposition of the remainder of the Upper Lias.

Junction Bed and Upper Lias Clay.—The Upper Lias portion of the Junction Bed consists of thinly bedded grey limestones with ferruginous, oolitic and conglomeratic bands yielding *Harpoceras*, *Hildoceras*, *Dactylioceras* and other ammonites. It therefore falls within the Serpentinum and Bifrons Zones. The deposits are greatly condensed and remanié fossils of several subzones may therefore be found in association. Although it is rarely more than 10 to 15 ft. thick, the Junction Bed is widely distributed, being found in the main escarpment from Doulting to Chard and also in the outliers of Pennard, Glastonbury, Brent Knoll and Dundry.

In the Eastern Mendips the Upper Lias is missing, partly as a result of the Bajocian Denudation (*see* Pl. XII), but the beds reappear south of Bath in the form of impersistent thin earthy and ferruginous limestones resting on the clays of the Lower Lias and overlain by the Midford Sands (Fig. 19). The beds remain in this form as far north as Old Sodbury, where the upper part passes into a pyritous sandy layer with *Hildoceras bifrons* at the base of the Cotteswold Sands, while the lower part consists of cream-coloured marl with *Harpoceras falcifer*. From this point northwards the Junction Bed passes into the sands and clays of the Cotswolds and eventually ceases to be a recognizable lithological unit.

Upper Lias Sands and Cephalopod Beds.—The lateral passage of the Junction Bed into sand and clay in the South Cotswolds is followed by even more rapid facies changes in the beds above. Before describing these, however, it is necessary to consider the general succession as proved in the escarpment between Old Sodbury and Stroud (*see* Figs. 17 and 19). Here the sandy limestones of the Scissum Beds (upper part of the Opalinum Zone) rest upon the Cephalopod Bed. The latter attains its maximum thickness of about 20 ft. in the Dursley district, where it consists of feruginous oolitic limestones and marls with abundant ammonites and belemnites. The stratigraphical importance of the Cephalopod Bed is due to its ammonite fauna which includes many forms of zonal value, e.g., *Grammoceras striatulum*, *Pseudogrammoceras struckmanni*, *Phlyseogrammoceras dispansum* and *Dumortieria moorei* (*see* Fig. 19).

Below the Cephalopod Bed lie some 200 ft. of fine yellow sand with doggers forming the Cotteswold Sands. These in turn rest upon the Junction Bed or Upper Lias Clay.

As the Cephalopod Bed is traced southwards from Stroud and Dursley towards Old Sodbury the basal layers with *Grammoceras thouarsense* and *G. striatulum* become sandy and then thicken as they pass into the Cotteswold Sands (Fig. 19). Near Bath the higher parts of the Cephalopod Bed are similarly affected, until in the Midford district south of Bath the bulk of the sand falls within the subzone of *Phlyseogrammoceras dispansum*. In general, therefore, the sandy facies as seen in the escarpment is older in the north than in the south.

Owing to the absence of the Upper Lias over the Mendip area we are not able to trace these facies changes continuously into Somerset. Where the beds are fully developed in south and east Somerset, however, it is found that the sandy facies, known as the Yeovil Sands, extends to the top of the Opalinum Zone. The uppermost part of the Yeovil Sands is therefore contemporaneous with the Scissum Beds of the Cotswolds, as demonstrated originally by S. S. Buckman.

The changes noted above apply only to the main escarpment of the Upper Lias running due north and south from Stroud to the hills above Sherborne.

(A 6283)

NIBLEY KNOLL, GLOUCESTERSHIRE. A VIEW OF THE COTSWOLD SCARP WITH SUBSIDIARY PLATFORM AT BASE FORMED BY HARD MIDDLE LIAS MARLSTONE ROCK

(A 6298)

THE AVON VALLEY NEAR LIMPLEY STOKE

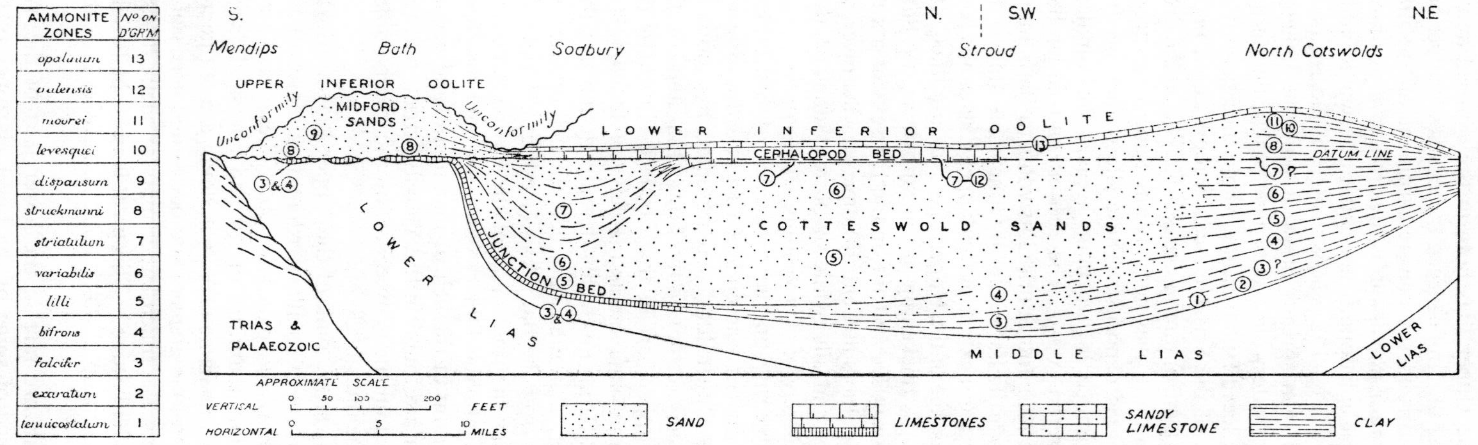

AMMONITE ZONES	No ON D'GR'M
opalinum	13
aalensis	12
moorei	11
levesquei	10
dispansum	9
struckmanni	8
striatulum	7
variabilis	6
lilli	5
bifrons	4
falcifer	3
exaratum	2
tenuicostatum	1

FIG. 19. *Diagrammatic section of the Upper Lias north of the Mendips, illustrating facies migration*
(The top of the striatulum subzone is taken as the datum-line)

When the whole of the Upper Lias both in the exposed and in the concealed areas is considered, the full significance of these facies changes becomes apparent. Thus to the north of Stroud the main escarpment of the Inferior Oolite and Upper Lias swings from a north-south direction to a north-easterly direction, while the outcropping Cephalopod Bed and Cotteswold Sands are seen to die away or pass into clay (Fig. 19). This change of facies first affects the lower part of the sands and then spreads upwards into the higher zones so that at Leckhampton Hill the Cotteswold Sands have practically disappeared (Fig. 19). Further north, in the Cleeve Hill area, the whole succession from the Marlstone Rock Bed to the base of the Scissum Beds is represented by Upper Lias clay. This formation attains a maximum thickness of 270 ft. in the Bredon Hill outlier

Borings for water in the Cotswolds have in some cases proved the nature of the concealed Upper Lias deposits. These show that the distribution of the Cotteswold Sands is limited to two main areas. The smaller area lies on or near the Vale of Moreton Axis. The second and larger belt extends along the western side of the Mid and South Cotswolds to Bath and effectively marks the shallows formed over the Bath Axis in Upper Lias times.

The relative thickness and extent of the Upper Lias sands is shown in Fig. 20, which illustrates the passage of the Upper Lias clay into the Cotteswold, Midford and Yeovil Sands and the thickening of the sands over the Bath Axis.

West of the Bath Axis at Down Cliff on the Dorset Coast and in the Glastonbury and Brent Knoll outliers in Central Somerset, the lower part of the Yeovil Sands passes into clay and silt, while in North Somerset the Upper Lias of Dundry Hill consists largely of clay yielding *Dumortieria*.

Much information bearing on the behaviour of the Jurassic rocks on the eastern margin of the district was obtained from a deep borehole at Westbury (Wiltshire). Here the Upper Lias is represented by about 50 ft. of muddy sands and dark sandy clay resting on the Lower Lias and overlain by the Lower Inferior Oolite. The upper part of these beds is shown by the occurrence of *Dumortieria* to be of the same age as the clays of Dundry Hill. If present at Westbury the Midford Sands are feebly developed, and it is therefore probable that in North Somerset, as in the Cotswolds, the belt of maximum development of the sandy facies lay over the Bath Axis (*see* Figs. 17 and 20).

South of the Mendips the thickening of the Yeovil Sands over a line drawn roughly from Doulting to the Dorset coast near Burton Bradstock indicates the southerly prolongation of the belt of maximum sand accumulation. Some 200 ft. of sand and silt are found in the Yeovil district, but near Beaminster in Dorset even this measurement is exceeded by the comparable Bridport Sands which swell up to a thickness of 300 ft.

The Yeovil Sands form the bulk of the Upper Lias in this area. The lower part of this series consists of small interdigitating lenses of impure limestone, blue-grey micaceous marl and pale grey silt. These pass upwards into strata which contain increasing quantities of silt and fine sand, while the top 50 to 60 ft. which alone merit the name of Yeovil Sands, are of fine to medium texture with rows of sandy limestone doggers and occasional lenses of shelly limestone. At Ham Hill, near Yeovil, a much larger mass of shelly limestone of this type is known as the 'Ham Hill Stone.' This great lens of shelly debris held together by a ferruginous cement is up to 90 ft. thick and passes laterally into sand with calcareous lenticles.

Well-preserved fossils are rare in the lower part of the Yeovil Sands, but evidence of the presence of some of the lower subzones of the Jurense Zone

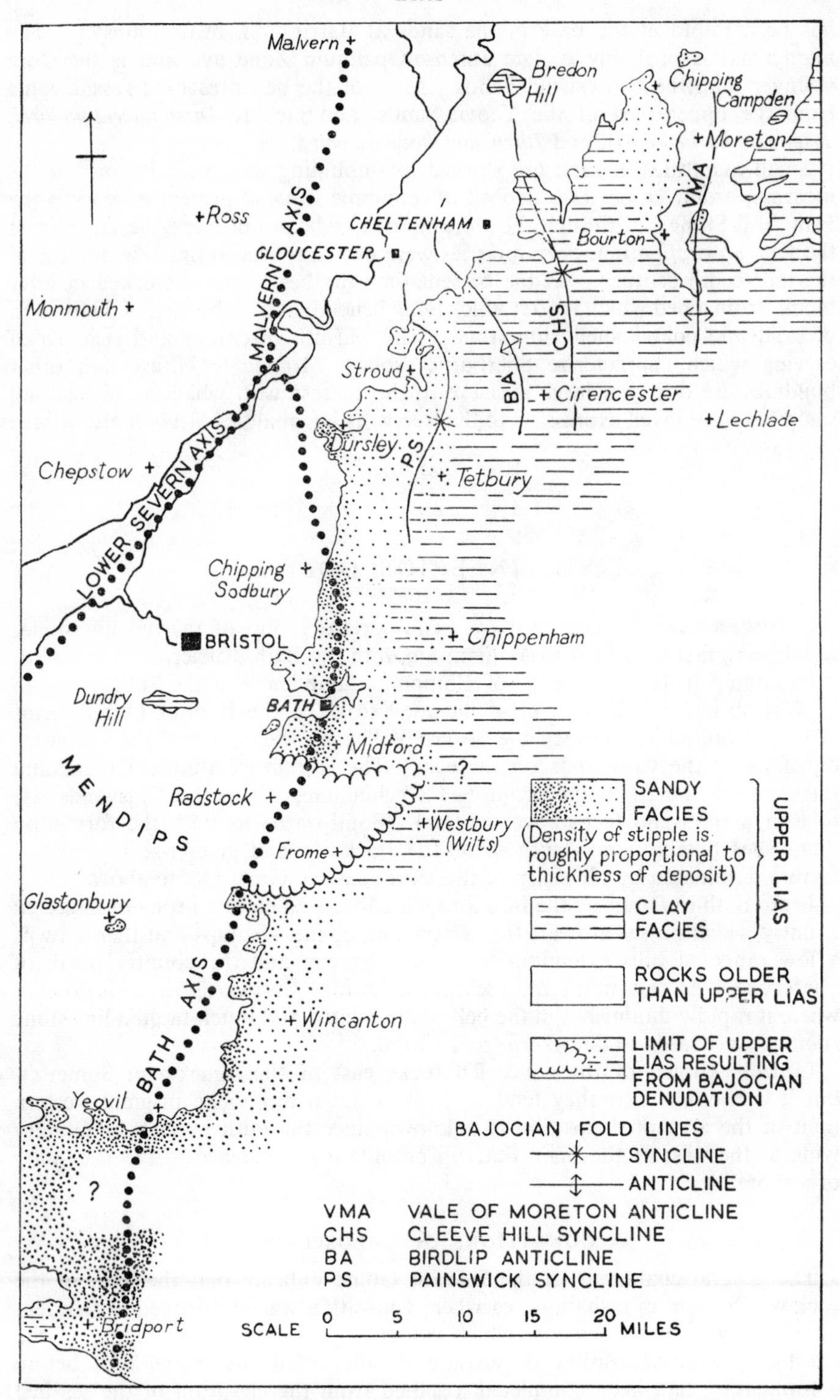

FIG. 20. *Sketch-map showing the relation of the sandy facies of the Upper Lias to the fold axes*

has been found at the base of the sands at Barrington, near Ilminster. The main mass is probably of late Jurense-Opalinum Zone age and is therefore younger than the Cotteswold Sands. Most of the best-preserved fossils come from the upper part of the Yeovil Sands, and include *Dumortieria moorei*, *Trigonia charlockensis*, and *Rhynchonelloidea cynica*.

Small quantities of sand are worked for moulding sand near Bitton but the most important Upper Lias deposit of economic value at present in work is the Ham Hill Stone. Although the working of this beautiful freestone dates from the Roman occupation, deep quarries were not commenced until the middle of the nineteenth century. At the present time the best stone is worked in huge blocks from a bed which is 50 ft. thick lying beneath an overburden of 30 to 40 ft. of sand and coarse shelly limestone. The warmth of colour and richness of carving which characterize Sherborne Abbey, Montacute House and other buildings are due in a large measure to the success with which architects and sculptors have given expression to the free-working qualities of Ham Hill Stone.

XII. INFERIOR OOLITE

THE UPPER LIAS is succeeded by an important group of marine limestones which were first identified by William Smith in the Bath district.

Extending from the vicinity of Chipping Campden into the country south of Wotton-under-Edge, the great indented scarp of the Inferior Oolite forms a natural boundary between the Severn Valley on the west and the limestone dip-slope of the Cotswolds on the east. The formation attains a maximum thickness of 300 ft. in the vicinity of Cheltenham, where the Cotswolds rise to over a thousand feet above sea-level. Southwards to Bath the formation diminishes to about one-tenth of its full thickness and gives rise to a minor feature dominated by the scarp of the more massive Great Oolite above.

From Bath to Doulting the Inferior Oolite forms an elevated tract of dissected country which passes athwart the eastern end of the Mendips and then crowns a low range of hills extending to Corton Beacon and the country north of Sherborne. At this point the escarpment swings westwards towards Yeovil, where it rapidly diminishes in the belt of attenuated and much-faulted limestone running westwards to Crewkerne and Chard.

Little is known of the concealed rocks east of the outcrop in Somerset, but it is thought that they tend to thicken down dip. The original western limit of the area of deposition is unknown since the outliers such as Dundry lying to the west of the main outcrop provide little evidence of the proximity of a shoreline.

CONDITIONS OF DEPOSITION

The general characters of the Inferior Oolite indicate that the bulk of the rock was formed in a shallow sea where deposition was interrupted at frequent intervals by earth-movements which caused slight warping or folding of the sea-floor. Non-deposition or erosion of the sediments, sometimes before consolidation had been completed, resulted from the elevation of the sea-bed into the zone of wave or current action. The movements are therefore recorded in the rocks as breaks in the succession known as non-sequences. In such cases there may be no recognizable angular disconformity.

Where widespread folding and erosion followed by general subsidence led to an extension of the area of deposition accompanied by overstepping of older by younger rocks, the term transgression is employed.

The presence of non-sequence is often, but not invariably, indicated by the occurrence of bored and oyster-covered surfaces, by limestone conglomerates, or by condensed deposits in which fossils of more than one faunal horizon are to be found often in a rolled condition with coatings of limonite or encrusting *Serpulae*.

The early classifications of the Inferior Oolite were based on lithology and mixed faunal assemblages, but it was shown by S. S. Buckman that these results were largely erroneous and that the key to the succession lay in the ammonite faunas, supplemented, in the Cotswolds, where ammonites are comparatively rare, by the use of brachiopods. On the basis of this pioneer work which has been much extended by later workers, the following classification has been evolved:

	Zones	*Subzones*
UPPER INFERIOR OOLITE	Parkinsoni	*Zigzagiceras zigzag* *Parkinsonia schloenbachi* *Strigoceras truelli* *Garantiana garantiana* *Strenoceras niortense*
	Upper Bajocian Transgression	
MIDDLE INFERIOR OOLITE	Humphriesianum	*Teloceras blagdeni* *Stephanoceras humphriesianum*
	Sauzei	*Otoites sauzei*
	Sowerbyi	*Witchellia laeviuscula* *Shirbuirnia trigonalis* *Hyperlioceras discites*
	Middle Bajocian Transgression	
LOWER INFERIOR OOLITE	Murchisonae	*Ludwigella concava* *Brasilia bradfordensis* *Ludwigia murchisonae* *Hudlestonia sinon*

THE BAJOCIAN TRANSGRESSIONS

The two principal periods of earth movement and their associated transgressions are well illustrated by the structure of the Inferior Oolite in the Cheltenham district (*see* Pl. XII).

Deposition of the Inferior Oolite in the Cotswolds commenced with the formation of the Lower Limestone and remained continuous until the close of Upper Freestone times (Fig. 21). Subsidence during this period appears to have been greatest in the Cheltenham area, which formed the centre of a broad basin of deposition where the maximum thickness of Lower Limestone and Freestone was built up. During this period the Painswick and Cleeve Hill synclines with the complementary Birdlip Anticline had not yet taken form.

Earth-movements in post-Upper Freestone times, however, led to the creation of a synclinal fold in the Cleeve Hill area accompanied by a slight general uplift followed by a change in conditions of sedimentation within the syncline which resulted in the deposition of the Harford Sands. The full extent of the area of deposition at this time cannot be estimated owing to the effect of later erosions,

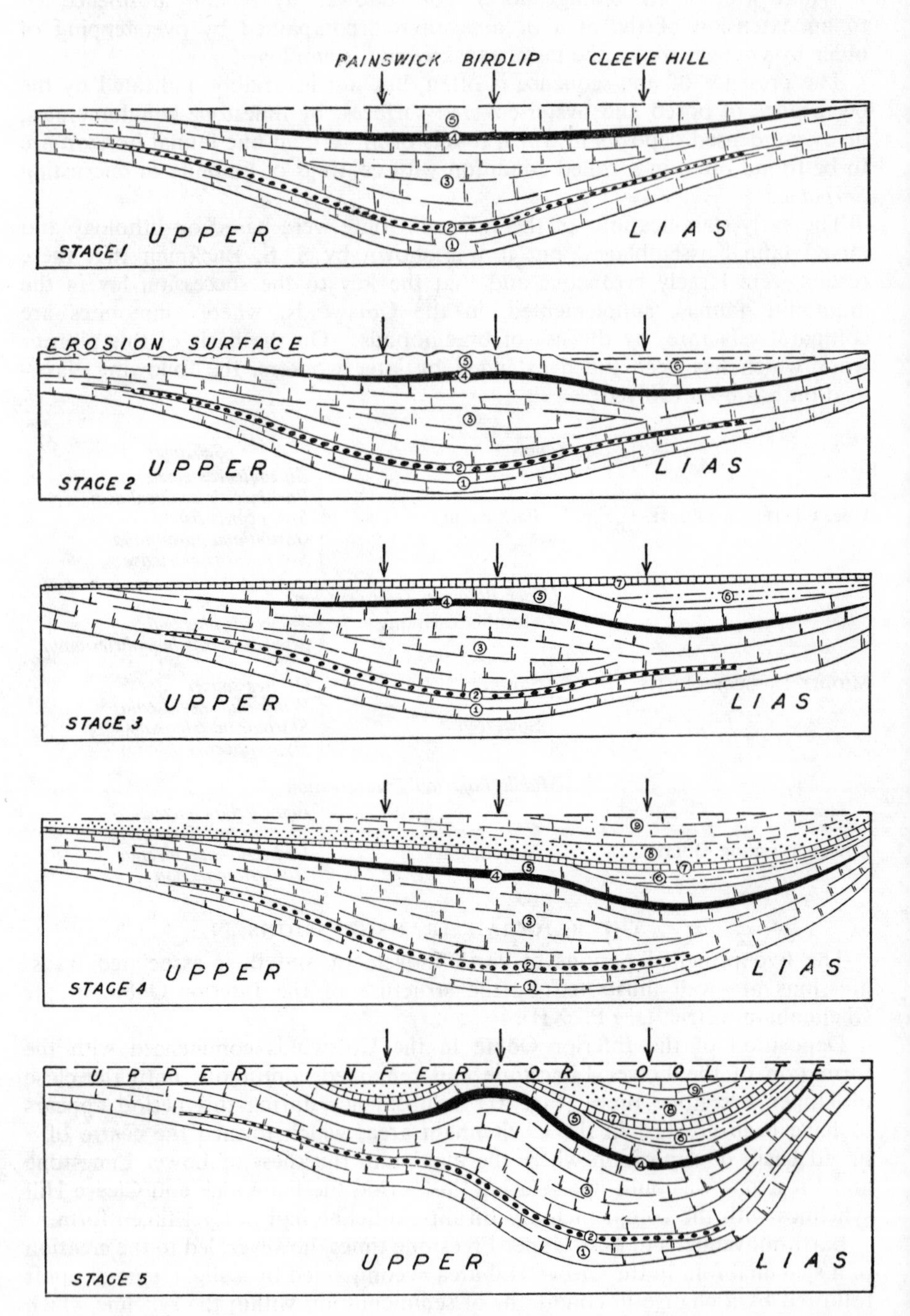

FIG. 21. *Diagrammatic representation of the depositional history of the Inferior Oolite as related to fold axes*

but within the Cleeve Hill Syncline the evidence is fairly clear for the Harford Sands only occur in a comparatively small area in the centre of the downfold. Moreover, they are succeeded and overlapped by the Snowshill Clay which, in turn, is overlapped by the Tilestones.

Deposition was therefore continuous in the centre of the syncline, though the nature of the sediments suggests that the waters were shallow and land-locked. The deposition of the sandy limestones known as the Tilestones evidently marks the influx of more open water and the entry of a limited marine fauna. The culminating point in this process was reached when the whole area was submerged beneath the waters of the Lower Trigonia Grit sea.

The resulting extension of the area of deposition constitutes the Middle Bajocian Transgression and marks the commencement of a new phase extending through Middle Inferior Oolite times when all the strata up to and including the Phillipsiana and Bourguetia Beds were laid down.

The thickening of the various divisions of the Middle Inferior Oolite as they are traced from Painswick into the Cleeve Hill Syncline suggests that once again subsidence was greatest in the latter area.

On the Cotswold evidence the date of the second and most impressive phase of folding can only be fixed as later than the Phillipsiana Beds and earlier than the Upper Trigonia Grit, since the intermediate strata are not represented north of the Mendips. At the close of Middle Inferior Oolite times, however, wide-spread folding of much greater intensity than any that had previously taken place, completed the shaping of the Painswick and Cleeve Hill synclines and the intervening Birdlip Anticline. Following this the entire Cotswold area was elevated and subjected to severe erosion. In the Birdlip Anticline this was carried down to the Freestone Beds, the Middle Inferior Oolite being completely removed.

Erosion and planation were followed by the subsidence of all the country from the Mendips to Moreton-in-Marsh, and the limestones of the Upper Trigonia Grit were laid down upon the bored and eroded surface of the older rocks.

The form of the denuded folds upon which the Upper Trigonia Grit was deposited in part of the Cotswolds is shown in Fig. 22, and the sequence of events described above is diagrammatically set out in Fig. 21.

EXPLANATION OF TEXT FIG. 21 (OPPOSITE)

Stage 1.—Continuous deposition in broad basin.

Stage 2.—Slight general uplift accompanied by erosion except in Cleeve Hill Syncline, where sandy and muddy sediments accumulated and filled the basin.

Stage 3.—General submergence beneath the Lower Trigonia Grit sea leading to Middle Bajocian Transgression.

Stage 4.—Deposition of remaining members of Middle Inferior Oolite probably in broad basin.

Stage 5.—Stronger folding giving rise to Birdlip Anticline and Painswick Syncline, succeeded first by denudation and then by general subsidence leading to Upper Bajocian Transgression.

KEY

1. Lower Limestone
2. Pea Grit
3. Lower Freestone
4. Oolite Marl
5. Upper Freestone
6. Harford Sands; Snowshill Clay; Tilestone
7. Lower Trigonia Grit
8. Buckmani and Gryphite Grits; Notgrove Freestone
9. Witchellia Grit; Phillipsiana-Bourguetia Beds

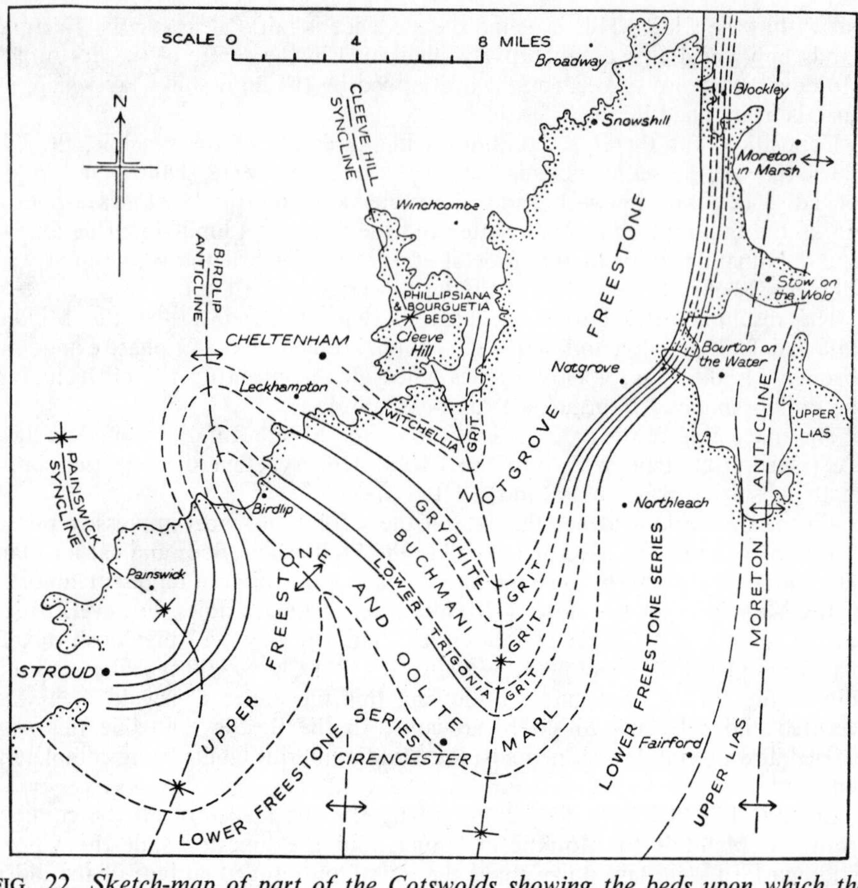

FIG. 22. *Sketch-map of part of the Cotswolds showing the beds upon which the Upper Inferior Oolite was deposited at the time of the Upper Bajocian Transgression*

(The stipple encloses the outcrop of the Inferior Oolite and later formations. The Lower and Middle Inferior Oolite outcrops are shown as they would appear if the Upper Inferior Oolite was removed. After S. S. Buckman, *Quart. Journ. Geol. Soc.*, 1901, with corrections by L. Richardson, *ibid.*, 1903.)

LOWER AND MIDDLE INFERIOR OOLITE

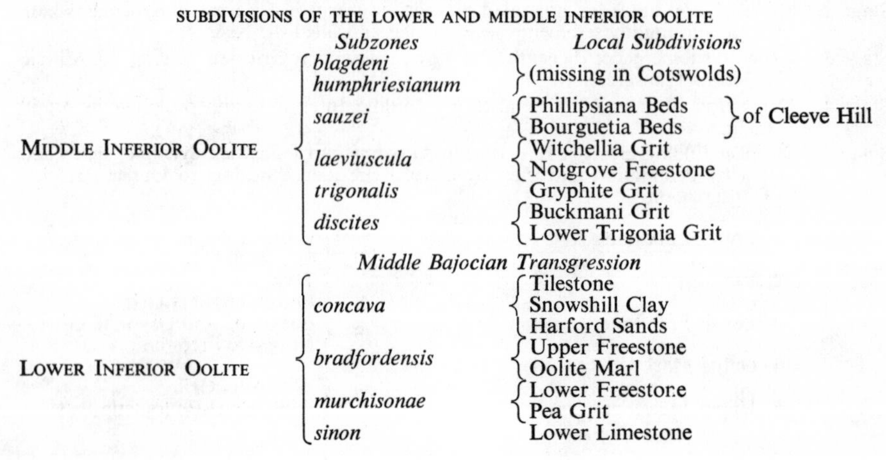

SUBDIVISIONS OF THE LOWER AND MIDDLE INFERIOR OOLITE

	Subzones	*Local Subdivisions*
MIDDLE INFERIOR OOLITE	*blagdeni* / *humphriesianum*	(missing in Cotswolds)
	sauzei	Phillipsiana Beds / Bourguetia Beds } of Cleeve Hill
	laeviuscula	Witchellia Grit / Notgrove Freestone
	trigonalis	Gryphite Grit
	discites	Buckmani Grit / Lower Trigonia Grit
	Middle Bajocian Transgression	
LOWER INFERIOR OOLITE	*concava*	Tilestone / Snowshill Clay / Harford Sands
	bradfordensis	Upper Freestone / Oolite Marl
	murchisonae	Lower Freestone / Pea Grit
	sinon	Lower Limestone

COTSWOLD AREA

In the Cotswolds the Lower and Middle Inferior Oolite reach their maximum thickness of 300 ft. (Pl. XII). When traced southwards towards Sodbury many of the subdivisions are seen to be attenuated or to have died out, whilst in the region of Bath the Middle and Lower Inferior Oolite are missing and the Upper Inferior Oolite rests non-sequentially on deposits of Upper Lias age.

The Lower Inferior Oolite is predominantly an oolitic freestone series, whilst the Middle Inferior Oolite comprises shelly splintery limestones known as 'Ragstones' or 'Grits.' The latter term is a misnomer, for they contain no appreciable quantity of quartz and are unlike any hard arenaceous deposit.

Lower Limestone.—The Upper Lias is succeeded by a group of some 20 to 30 ft. of rather unfossiliferous oolitic limestones which reach their maximum development near Stroud, where they have been much quarried. When locally conglomeratic, as in the Stroud district, they are termed 'Dapple Beds.'

Pea Grit.—In the Cheltenham area the Pea Grit is a pisolitic limestone, the top part being exceptionally coarse-grained and rubbly. Many of the pisoliths have been formed by the growth of a tubular organism around an inorganic nucleus.

The Pea Grit contains an abundance of small fossils such as sea urchins and corals, while the brachiopods include *Pseudoglossothyris simplex* and *Plectoidothyris plicata.* Typical sections are to be seen on Crickley Hill near Birdlip and at Leckhampton Hill, Cheltenham. Near Stroud the Pea Grit is thinner and south of Dursley it cannot be distinguished as a separate formation. Under these conditions the Lower Limestone and the Lower Freestone are not separable and are termed the 'Freestone Series.'

Northwards and eastwards of the Cleeve Hill—Stroud area the Pea Grit passes laterally into a warm brown freestone known as 'Guiting Stone' which has been extensively worked on the western margin of the Cotswolds as at Temple Guiting and Stanway, and on the east at Bourton-on-the-Hill. This rock is known as 'Yellow Guiting,' the overlying 'White Guiting' being the equivalent of the Lower Freestone.

Lower Freestone.—The Lower Freestone, which overlies the Pea Grit, is important as forming the well-known Cheltenham Building Stone which at Leckhampton Hill reaches 130 ft. in thickness and was once extensively quarried. Near Chipping Campden the freestone is quarried under the name of 'Campden Stone.' The beds consist of pale oolite resembling Bath Stone in texture, and, being relatively free from shell fragments, are capable of being easily dressed and carved.

Oolite Marl and Upper Freestone.—Resting upon the Lower Freestone in the Mid and North Cotswold area is the richly fossiliferous Oolite Marl, consisting of ooliths packed in chalky white marl some 10 ft. thick. The most characteristic fossil is *Plectothyris fimbria*, whilst lamellibranchs and micro-organisms abound. The overlying Upper Freestone is harder and more oolitic though this too may have numerous soft marly bands as at Frith Quarry, near Stroud. Thus from Stroud southwards, the Oolite Marl and Upper Freestone cannot be separated. The Upper Freestone is often unsuitable for building, owing to its frequently soft and marly character. Fossils are not very abundant, though '*Rhynçhonella*' *tatei* occurs in the top part of the bed.

Harford Sands, Snowshill Clay and Tilestone.—This group of beds occupies a restricted area in the North Cotswolds and is best seen in the region between Winchcombe and Broad Campden.

The lowest member, the Harford Sands, consists of some 9 ft. of pale brown quartz-sand frequently hardened to form doggers and sand-burrs. Mineralogically they are characterized by abundant grains of sphene and rare kyanite. The sands were formerly dug on Cleeve Hill and carried to the Staffordshire potteries.

The Snowshill Clay comprises some 15 ft. of stiff chocolate-coloured clay which reaches its maximum thickness at Blockley. The overlying Tilestone is also best developed in the Blockley area, where it consists of sandy oolitic limestone, locally containing rolled pebbles of oolite.

Lower Trigonia Grit.—This basal member of the Middle Inferior Oolite was deposited upon the eroded surface of underlying strata, and its base is frequently conglomeratic. The deposit consists of rubbly, often ironshot, limestone crowded with fossils, particularly lamellibranchs such as *Trigonia*. A coral bed with *Chorisastraea* occurs near the base.

Buckmani and Gryphite Grits.—The Buckmani Grit is a yellow sandy limestone (with *Lobothyris buckmani*) which reaches a maximum thickness of 17 ft. It passes upwards into the Gryphite Grit, which is a massive, bedded sandy limestone characterized by an abundance of the oyster *Gryphaea*.

Notgrove Freestone.—This division has a wide extent in the North and Central Cotswolds, where it attains a thickness of 15 to 25 ft. It consists of hard, white, fine-textured limestone, locally crowded with shells of *Variamussium pumilum*.

Witchellia Grit.—This consists of thin, grey-brown, ironshot limestone containing ammonites in greater abundance than the lower beds.

Phillipsiana and Bourguetia Beds.—These beds, representing the highest zone of the Middle Inferior Oolite preserved in the Cotswold and Dundry areas, are confined to the Cleeve Hill Syncline. They consist of hard, shelly limestones yielding '*Terebratula*' *phillipsiana* and the gastropod *Bourguetia striata*. Many of the brachiopod shells are beekitized.

DUNDRY AND THE AREA SOUTH OF THE MENDIPS

The main outcrop of the Inferior Oolite from Old Sodbury to Bruton shows Upper Inferior Oolite resting upon Upper Lias or older strata (Pl. XII). Any Lower or Middle Inferior Oolite which may have been deposited was removed by erosion prior to the deposition of the later rocks.

At Dundry Hill, however, in the most westerly outlier north of the Mendips, about 10 ft. of Lower Inferior Oolite and 7 ft. of Middle Inferior Oolite are preserved in a shallow syncline beneath the upper beds. The close similarity between the Dundry rocks and fossils and those of the contemporaneous strata in Dorset and east Somerset adds an interest transcending the purely palaeontological aspect of the Dundry faunas, for the evidence indicates that Dundry and the Dorset areas formed part of the same depositional and zoological province during Lower and Middle Inferior Oolite times.

Sandy ferruginous beds, and hard limestones with limonitic ooliths (' ironshots ') are the typical Dundry rock-types. Of the fossils, brachiopods are common, while all groups of the mollusca are abundant. Unlike the contiguous Cotswolds, Dundry resembles distant Dorset in that ammonites are numerous and well-preserved.

In the Cotswolds ammonites are rare and prior to burial the shells have often been drifted into position in a damaged condition. At a few horizons, as in the Witchellia Grit, ammonites occur in a fair state of preservation, while there are also some brachiopods common to both the Dundry and the Dorset areas. On the basis of such common occurrences S. S. Buckman established the correlation of Dundry and the Cotswolds.

Middle and Lower Inferior Oolite rocks are also preserved south of the Mendips in a shallow syncline at Cole and Bruton in east Somerset, and in the Yeovil and Crewkerne districts (Pl. XII).

The Cole Syncline is interesting in that the blagdeni subzone is present beneath the Upper Inferior Oolite. This is the highest subzone of the Middle Inferior Oolite and its preservation.therefore fixes the date of the upper Bajocian Transgression.

In the Yeovil district the succession is extremely attenuated and incomplete, the thinnest known development being over the Bath Axis at Yeovil Junction where the Upper Inferior Oolite rests upon 6 ins. of Middle and 15 ins. of Lower Inferior Oolite (Fig. 23). West of Yeovil Junction the sequence is thicker and more complete, but at Haslebury Mill, 7 miles west of Yeovil, Upper Inferior Oolite is once more found resting on Upper Lias.

Thin variable deposits of Lower Inferior Oolite appear in the Crewkerne district where they include a blue ironshot limestone of the same age (Murchisonae Zone) as the well-known ' Red Bed ' of the Dorset Coast.

UPPER INFERIOR OOLITE

The Upper Inferior Oolite is subdivided as follows:

Subzones	North Cotswolds	Dundry and S. Cotswolds	Milborne Port —Yeovil	Crewkerne
zigzag	Chipping Norton Limestone	Zigzag Bed	Crackment Limestone	'The Scroff' and Zigzag Bed
schloenbachi	Clypeus Grit	Rubbly Beds and Anabacia Limestones	Rubbly Limestone Beds	Microzoa and Sponge Beds
truellei	Absent	Doulting Stone Upper Coral Bed	Sherborne Building Stone and Astarte obliqua Bed	Truellei Bed
	—	Dundry Freestone		
garantiana	Upper Trigonia Grit	Ironshot limestone and conglomerate		Thin Limestone
niortense	Absent		Niortense Bed	Absent

As a result of the widespread folding and erosion which took place prior to the deposition of the Upper Inferior Oolite the latter is found to rest on a variety of formations (*see* Pl. XII). These range from the Middle Inferior Oolite to the Lias, and in the case of the Eastern Mendips, the Trias and the Palaeozoic. Only one small area in south-east Somerset escaped the full severity of these movements and here in the Milborne Port district thin sandy and ferruginous rocks with *Strenoceras niortense* represent the earliest deposits of the Upper Inferior Oolite.

In this connection it may be observed that the Niortense Beds are not found over or to the west of the Bath Axis. Furthermore it is thought that the beds are overlapped westwards by the conformable sandy limestones of the garantiana subzone above, and that their preservation has been determined by the form of the basin in which they were laid down and not by subsequent folding and erosion.

DUNDRY AND COTSWOLD AREA

Upper Trigonia Grit.—Over the Cotswold area the Upper Trigonia Grit forms the basal member of the Upper Inferior Oolite and consists of some 7 ft. of grey splintery ragstone resting on a bored and eroded surface of Lower or Middle Inferior Oolite. Ammonites are very rare in the Cotswolds but brachiopods are abundant and include '*Terebratula globata*,' *Acanthothyris spinosa* and '*Rhynchonella*' *hampenensis*. Lamellibranchs including *Pleuromya*, *Pholadomya*, *Trichites* and *Trigonia* are also common, the latter being in the form of casts which are so numerous as to give the rock its name.

At Dundry the equivalent beds are only about a foot thick but they are fossiliferous and yield *Garantiana* and *Rhactorhynchia subtetrahedra*.

In the neighbourhood of the Mendips as at Maes Knoll, Timsbury Sleight and Doulting the Upper Trigonia Grit is represented by a thin conglomerate, while it is missing over the Mendip and Vale of Moreton axes.

Dundry Freestone.—At Dundry Hill, above the equivalent of the Upper Trigonia Grit, there is a local development of massive limestone, known as Dundry Freestone. This deposit is only 4 ft. thick at the eastern end of the hill but at the western end it attains a maximum thickness of 27 ft. St. Mary Redcliffe and other Bristol churches were wholly or partly built of this freestone but the quarries are now abandoned, much of the best stone having been long since worked out.

Upper Coral Bed.—Overlying the Dundry Freestone is the Upper Coral Bed. This easily recognized formation consists of up to 7½ ft. of crystalline and siliceous rubbly limestone and marl. It contains *Isastraea* and other corals as well as echinoderms and brachiopods such as *Zeilleria waltoni* and *Aulacothyris carinata*. Although the Upper Coral Bed is impersistent it is said to be traceable from near Bruton, south of the Mendips, as far north as Stroud.

Many of the fossils are beekitized and small irregular wisps and patches of chalcedony investing geodes lined with small quartz crystals are common in the Coral Bed and the upper part of the underlying Freestone.

Doulting Stone, Anabacia Limestones and Rubbly Beds.—Above the Upper Coral bed lies a deposit of white, rather massive limestone, known as Doulting Stone, which is overlain by flaggy white oolite in which the small coral *Anabacia complanata* is abundant. This in turn is succeeded by white rubbly limestones, termed the Rubbly Beds. Traced northwards, the Doulting Stone thins, and in the Mid and North Cotswolds the three formations merge into a highly characteristic deposit known as Clypeus Grit.

Clypeus Grit.—The name Clypeus Grit is derived from the profusion of the large sea-urchin *Clypeus sinuatus* which characterizes the formation. Around Stow-on-the-Wold this fossil is so abundant that when fields are cleaned the heaps of stones are found to be largely made up of damaged specimens. The rock itself is highly distinctive, being almost a pisolite with large yellow granules set in a buff chalky matrix.

Chipping Norton Limestone.—In the North Cotswolds a thin clay parting separates the Clypeus Grit from the overlying Chipping Norton Limestone which reaches a maximum thickness of some 20 ft. in the heart of the North

Cotswolds. This deposit exhibits considerable lithological variation. Where typically developed it consists of buff, hard, rather splintery oolite containing minute specks of lignite; elsewhere the beds are flaggy and have been worked in the past for flagstones. Decalcification has in some cases reduced it to sand.

Fossils are not common. The lamellibranch *Lima cardiiformis* occurs in most exposures, while obscure plant remains and occasional saurian bones, e.g. *Megalosaurus*, *Teleosaurus* and *Steneosaurus* are not infrequently found.

Ammonites are exceedingly rare, but those that occur suggest that the Chipping Norton Limestone falls within the zigzag subzone and is therefore to be correlated with the Zigzag Bed and the Crackment Limestone.

MENDIP—DOULTING AREA

When traced southwards from Bath the lower part of the Upper Inferior Oolite becomes thinner and eventually disappears (*see* Pl. XII). Only the Doulting Stone and higher beds cross the Mendip Axis and where these are seen in the deep valleys west of Frome they rest unconformably upon the Carboniferous Limestone of the Eastern Mendips.

Magnificent sections showing almost horizontal Upper Inferior Oolite resting on a bored and planed off surface of steeply-dipping Carboniferous Limestone are exposed at Vallis Vale near Frome. Traces of Lower Lias and Rhaetic occur in some places between the Inferior Oolite and the Carboniferous Limestone.

Southwards by Doulting to Batcombe the surface of the Palaeozoic rocks falls away steeply and higher beds of the Lias appear beneath the Doulting Stone. Thus at Alham about 50 ft. of Doulting Stone with a conglomeratic base rest on micaceous silts of Upper Lias age.

Near Doulting the railway cutting and quarries show typical Doulting Stone consisting of shelly and oolitic limestone and freestone in which crinoid fragments and oolite grains are embedded in a matrix of crystalline calcite. Considerable lateral variation may be seen in the exposed rock faces and there is much current-bedding.

Though not so readily carved as Bath or Ham Hill Stone, Doulting Stone is very durable. It was used in the construction of many fine mediaeval buildings, Wells Cathedral with its great twelfth century west front being the most outstanding example.

DOULTING—CREWKERNE

Between Doulting and Milborne Port the Upper Inferior Oolite contains little of interest. Near Castle Cary the garantiana subzone is represented by about 10 ft. of brown ferruginous building stone with *Parkinsonia raricostata* and abundant *Acanthothyris spinosa.* The remainder of the formation consists of limestone of equivalent age to the Doulting Stone but of little economic value as a building stone.

Turning now to the country around Sherborne and Milborne Port we find a great increase in the thickness of the Upper Inferior Oolite. At the base is the ' Sherborne Building Stone ' up to 20 ft. in thickness, overlain by rubbly limestone and marl. *Garantiana garantiana*, *Nautilus* and nests of *Sphaeroidothyris sphaeroidalis* occur, the latter being known to the older quarrymen as ' gooseberries.' Among other interesting fossils the Sherborne Building Stone has yielded the remains of a dinosaur, *Megalosaurus bucklandi*, and the cone of an

Araucarian pine, *Araucaria cleminshawi*, is also thought to have come from these beds.

Above the Sherborne Building Stone lies the 'Crackment Limestone,' a formation which is typically developed in the Milborne Port area. The latter is composed of pale grey or dirty white limestone with clay partings and is over 20 ft. thick in its fullest development. Besides *Zigzagiceras*, the fossils include ammonites belonging to the genera *Procerites*, *Morphoceras* and *Oppelia*. Much confusion has arisen in the past through the misidentification of the Oppelid ammonites of the zigzag subzone with *Oppelia fusca* of the Lower Fuller's Earth Clay. L. F. Spath has shown, however, that the species in the zigzag subzone are not conspecific with *Oppelia fusca* which is a later form than those occurring in the Crackment Limestone.

To the west of Sherborne the Upper Inferior Oolite thins towards Yeovil and the Bath Axis. The Sherborne Building Stone and the overlying rubbly limestones become more and more attenuated and at Halfway House are represented by the 'Fossil Bed' and Astarte obliqua Bed—two condensed fossiliferous limestones which together total only 18 ins. Around Yeovil the garantiana and truellei subzones are seldom more than a few inches thick and can only be recognized with great difficulty.

A similar westerly thinning can be observed in the case of the Crackment Limestone, which is only 5 ft. thick near Yeovil and at Haslebury Mill, near Haslebury Plucknett, is represented by about 4 in. of rubbly white limestone and clay with *Morphoceras*. In this condition it is known as the Zigzag Bed, and constitutes a useful datum line in the Crewkerne and Bridport districts.

CONDITIONS OF DEPOSITION OF THE UPPER INFERIOR OOLITE

The variations in thickness and lithology of the Upper Inferior Oolite can be related to fold lines as in the case of the Lower and Middle Inferior Oolite (*q.v.*). The effects are not perhaps so strongly marked but the Bath and Mendip axes, the Cleeve Hill Syncline, the Vale of Moreton Anticline, and other minor fold axes, all appear to have exerted some influence upon the nature and amount of sediment accumulated.

XIII. GREAT OOLITE SERIES

THE GREAT OOLITE SERIES may be regarded as embracing all the formations between the Inferior Oolite and the Cornbrash, and therefore includes the Fuller's Earth, Stonesfield Slate, Great Oolite Limestone and Forest Marble. The stratigraphy of this series like that of the Lias and Inferior Oolite was first worked out by William Smith in the Bath district, which is therefore to be regarded as the type area.

The principal subdivisions of the Great Oolite Series are given in the accompanying table but it should be emphasized that the correlation of this extremely variable series of deposits is difficult, largely owing to the rarity of ammonites.

For descriptive purposes the Great Oolite Series may be conveniently divided into two main groups, the line of separation being placed at the base of the Boueti Bed and Bradford Clay.

FULLER'S EARTH, STONESFIELD SLATE AND GREAT OOLITE LIMESTONE

The three main facies of the lower group are given stratigraphical names. The Fuller's Earth, so-called because of the occurrence of a thin bed of fuller's earth in the Bath district, is predominantly a clay formation. It attains a thickness of more than 400 ft. in East Somerset but is rarely more than 100 to 150 ft. near Bath and may thin to 20 to 30 ft. in parts of the Cotswolds.

The Stonesfield Slate is a calcareo-arenaceous deposit consisting of flaggy, sandy and oolitic limestones best developed in the Mid and North Cotswolds where it overlies or is interbedded with the top of the attenuated Fuller's Earth Clay of that district. It has not been identified south of Sodbury.

SUGGESTED CORRELATION OF THE GREAT OOLITE SERIES

Ammonite Zones	Characteristic Brachiopods	Sodbury—North Cotswolds	Bath—Sodbury	Somerset
Wagnericeras arbustigerum	*Epithyris marmorea*	Forest Marble (Wychwood Beds)	Forest Marble and Hinton Sands	
	Epithyris bathonica and *Digonella digona*	Bradford Beds	Bradford Clay and Acton Turville Beds	Boueti Bed
	Epithyris oxonica	Kemble Beds White Limestone	Upper Great Oolite Limestone including Bath Stone	Upper Fuller's Earth Clay
Oppelia fusca	*Wattonithyris wattonensis*		Lower Great Oolite Limestone	Wattonensis Bed
		Hampen Marly Beds		Upper Fuller's Earth Clay
	Ornithella bathonica and *Rhynchonelloidella smithii*	Taynton and Minchinhampton Freestones		Fuller's Earth Rock
		Stonesfield Slate Fuller's Earth Clay	Lower Fuller's Earth Clay	

The Great Oolite Limestone, on the other hand, consists primarily of hard, white, shelly oolitic limestones and freestones in which current-bedding is often strongly developed. In the Box—Cirencester area the average thickness of these limestones is 100 to 125 ft.

A further limestone type found in the upper part of the Great Oolite Limestone consists of hard, grey, flaggy current-bedded limestone largely composed of shell debris.

This rock closely resembles the shelly limestone of the Forest Marble with which it has been confused. The term 'Forest Marble' has been applied indiscriminately to beds both above and below the Bradford Clay, and in order to avoid this difficulty the beds below the Bradford Clay have been named Kemble Beds while those above have been distinguished as Wychwood Beds.

The strata described above crop out in a wide belt running along the eastern side of the region from Dorset to Oxfordshire and beyond. This belt may be divided into two provinces lying north and south respectively of an east-west line drawn roughly midway between Bath and Frome. The northern province includes Bath and the Cotswolds where the Great Oolite Limestones are developed. In the southern province, on the other hand, the equivalent rocks consist mainly of clay.

DORSET—SOMERSET PROVINCE

The general sequence in this province is shown in Fig. 23.

Lower Fuller's Earth.—Resting on the Upper Inferior Oolite limestones, the Lower Fuller's Earth Clay has at its base a thin but remarkably constant oyster bed characterized by *Ostrea knorri*. This bed has been found at various points along the outcrop extending over the whole province and northwards to Cooper's Hill near Gloucester. Since the Knorri Bed is continuous over the Bath and Mendip axes it would appear that, at the commencement of Fuller's Earth times, the sea-bed formed an almost even surface at shallow depth.

In North and East Somerset, the Fuller's Earth clays can be separated into upper and lower divisions lying above and below the Fuller's Earth Rock. Where, however, the Fuller's Earth Rock cannot be detected as in the Halstock district, south-west of Yeovil, a series of thin limestones and marls known as the Wattonensis Bed, lying at a higher horizon than the Fuller's Earth Rock, provides the only mappable line on which subdivision can be based.

Near the top of the Lower Fuller's Earth Clay occurs another oyster bed composed of the sickle-shaped *Ostrea acuminata*. This bed extends from near Yeovil to the South Cotswolds but, like the Fuller's Earth Rock, has not been found in the Halstock area nor in Dorset, and probably dies away over the Bath Axis at Yeovil (Fig. 23).

Fuller's Earth Rock.—As typically developed in the main outcrop extending from Bath to the Sherborne district of Dorset this bed consists of rubbly fossiliferous grey limestone with a rich brachiopod fauna. The dominant fossils are *Rhynchonelloidella smithii* and Ornithellids of which *Ornithella bathonica* is a common example. Ammonites are less abundant but include *Tulites subcontractus* and *Morrisiceras morrisi*. The Fuller's Earth Rock rarely exceeds 35 ft. in thickness. South of Yeovil it dies out or passes into impersistent nodular beds in the Halstock area.

Upper Fuller's Earth Clay and Wattonensis Bed.—Above the Fuller's Earth Rock a thick and monotonous clay series is only relieved by one thin band of marl and argillaceous limestone. The latter is known as the Wattonensis Bed since it yields the characteristic terebratulid *Wattonithyris wattonensis* and it differs from the Fuller's Earth Rock in that Ornithellids are rare or absent. The chief importance of this bed lies in the fact that it provides a means of correlating at least a part of the Great Oolite Series. It indicates that the so-called Fuller's Earth Rock of Dorset and the Halstock area which contains a Wattonensis Bed fauna is in fact younger than the Fuller's Earth Rock or East Somerset and the Mendip area.

The main mass of the Fuller's Earth Clay is seldom exposed for study and the stratigraphical ranges of many of the brachiopods and ammonites are therefore uncertain. It is known, however, that the ammonite *Oppelia fusca* occurs immediately beneath the Wattonensis Bed at Halstock, and the rocks

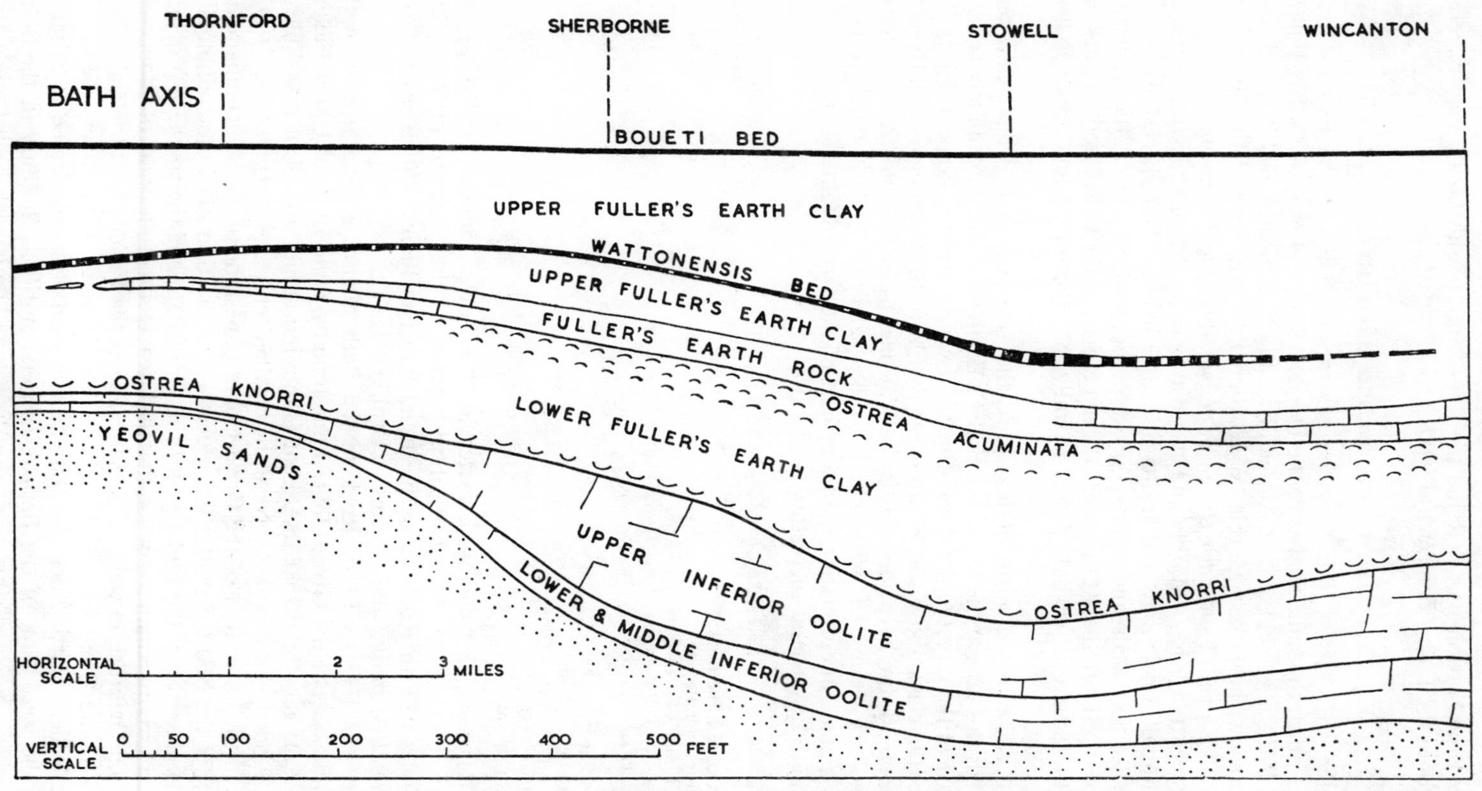

FIG. 23. *Section to show the stratigraphy of the Fuller's Earth in the southern province*

between the Wattonensis Bed and the top of the Inferior Oolite may therefore fall within the Fusca Zone (*sensu lato*).

BATH—COTSWOLD PROVINCE

In the area east of Radstock the general succession in the Fuller's Earth Clay is much the same as that of the Dorset—Somerset province. The Fuller's Earth Rock is present and at Ammerdown the Wattonensis Bed is found some 80 ft. below the Forest Marble (Wychwood Beds) the base of the latter being marked by a thin band with *Digonella digona* and *Chlamys vagans*.

Between the Forest Marble and the Wattonensis Bed, *Epithyris oxonica* has been found in pale marl and earthy limestone bands. This species also occurs in the Kemble Beds and White Limestone of the Cotswolds. Its occurrence suggests therefore that at this point the upper part of the Great Oolite Limestone of Bath and the Cotswolds passes laterally into the top of the Upper Fuller's Earth Clay.

At Wellow to the north of Radstock, the Wattonensis Bed has again been seen, but this time at the top of the Fuller's Earth Clay and immediately beneath the base of the Great Oolite Limestones. It would therefore appear that in this district the clays above the Wattonensis Bed have been completely replaced by limestone. From here northwards the Wattonensis Bed has not yet been found and at Bath we are left with only the more persistent Fuller's Earth Rock to act as a guide in correlating the lower part of the Great Oolite Series.

At Bath the general succession is as follows:

		Approximate thickness in ft.
Great Oolite Limestone:		
Limestone and oolite	seen for	30
Upper Fuller's Earth Clay:		
Clay with thin bands of marly and oolitic limestone		10
Fuller's Earth Bed		6
Clay		60
Fuller's Earth Rock:		
Rubbly limestone		10
Lower Fuller's Earth Clay:		
Clay		30

In this area the general characters of the Lower Fuller's Earth Clay and Fuller's Earth Rock are identical with those of the southern province, and the Fuller's Earth Rock yields the usual fauna including *Morrisiceras*, *Rhynchonelloidella smithii* and swarms of Ornithellids.

Since the Fuller's Earth Rock in the Bath district is separated from the overlying beds of the Great Oolite Limestone by some 70 ft. of Upper Fuller's Earth Clay it follows that the Great Oolite limestones are all of post-Fuller's Earth Rock age in this area. Nevertheless the occurrence of *Tulites* and *Morrisiceras* in the lower part of the Great Oolite Limestone of the Minchinhampton district of the Mid Cotswolds introduces a complication since these ammonites are characteristic of the Fuller's Earth Rock of Bath and the southern province. This led S. S. Buckman to suggest that the Great Oolite Limestones of Gloucestershire and Oxfordshire were of the same age as the Fuller's Earth Rock. Work by Arkell and Donovan (1952) tends to support some of Buckman's views.

The Fuller's Earth Rock can only be identified with any degree of certainty along the west flank of the Bath Axis as far north as Sodbury in the South Cotswolds. North of this point thin limestone bands have been found in the

Fuller's Earth Clay, but the complete fauna with *Morrisiceras* and the characteristic Ornithellids has not yet been detected.

In the Cotswolds the Fuller's Earth Clay is thin and is overlain by the Stonesfield Slate or Passage Beds, which yield the ammonite *Gracilisphinctes* both in Oxfordshire and at Sodbury. This suggests that the Stonesfield Slate is of generally constant age over the intervening area. If, therefore, the lower part of the Great Oolite Limestone of the Cotswolds is a diachronous facies replacing the Fuller's Earth Rock of Somerset, it is apparent that the maximum shift in the facies migration must take place over the Bath Axis in the South Cotswolds. On this view the development of the Stonesfield Slate and Great Oolite Limestone facies of the Fuller's Earth would parallel that of the sandy facies of the Upper Lias.

In the southern province there are few rocks of economic importance in the Great Oolite Series, but in the northern province a number of deposits have important uses and these are therefore briefly described below.

Commercial Fuller's Earth.—The Fuller's Earth Bed in the Upper Fuller's Earth has long been exploited in the vicinity of Combe Hay and Midford where it averages some 6 ft. in thickness. At the present time the Fuller's Earth Bed is worked both in a small opencast pit at Vernham Wood and from underground levels driven into the steep hillsides below the limestone plateau south of Bath. The raw material differs from the other clays of the Great Oolite Series in its lack of plasticity and its property of swelling up when shaken with an excess of water. This feature is associated with clay minerals of the montmorillonite family to whose presence the qualities of the Fuller's Earth are thought to be due.

The early exploitation of the Fuller's Earth deposits of North Somerset was due largely to the demands of the West of England woollen industry where the earth was employed in the cleansing of wool and woollen cloth. At the present time it has many additional uses, as for example in the manufacture of toilet preparations and the refining of fats and oils.

Stonesfield Slate Beds.—In the North and Mid Cotswolds these beds consist of sandy, shelly and oolitic limestones with partings of sandy shale. The total thickness is rarely more than 25 ft. The ' Slates ' which were formerly worked for roofing tiles were obtained from the Slate Bed or ' Pendle,' a band of fissile sandy limestone situated near the base of the beds.

In the South Cotswolds the Stonesfield Slate Beds form a passage series between the Great Oolite Limestone above and the Fuller's Earth Clay below. East of Sodbury they are about 35 ft. in thickness and yield *Gracilisphinctes gracilis*, an ammonite which is found in the Stonesfield Slate of Oxfordshire. Other fossils which characterize the Stonesfield Slate are *Ostrea acuminata*, *Trigonia impressa*, and numerous vertebrate remains including pterodactyls, dinosaurs, crocodiles and small primitive mammals.

Bath, Minchinhampton and Taynton Freestones.—Above the Stonesfield Slate Beds of the Cotswolds and the Lower Great Oolite limestones of the eastern part of the Bath district there lies a group of white freestones and current-bedded oolites which have yielded some of the best known of the Jurassic building stones. The most celebrated of these is Bath Stone, but Minchinhampton and Taynton Stone were also famous in former days.

The present Bath Stone workings are situated in the Corsham district of West Wiltshire, a little to the east of the boundary of the region, but freestone has also been quarried at Combe Down nearer Bath. At Box and Corsham the stone is worked in underground galleries approached by inclines driven through the Forest Marble. Though it hardens on exposure to the air, when newly dug it is soft enough to be cut with a saw, and is therefore ideal for mouldings.

Bath Stone was used by the Romans in the construction of their hot baths, was employed in many mediaeval buildings and is still widely used to-day. The attractive appearance of the city of Bath is due largely to the consistent use of Bath Stone through the ages, more particularly in the eighteenth century when the magnificent crescents were built.

In the Mid Cotswolds current-bedded oolitic freestones with shelly layers were extensively quarried at Minchinhampton. Similar beds were also quarried at Taynton, but to-day most of these quarries are completely overgrown. Taynton Quarries furnished the freestone for some of the earliest buildings in Oxford.

White Limestone and Hampen Marly Beds.—In the Mid and North Cotswolds the freestones are overlain by the White Limestone. In this division there are two principal rock types: whitish oolitic limestone alternating with marl; and very hard, splintery, fine-grained limestone. The latter is frequently riddled with branching cavities, possibly due to the solution of corals, and is known as 'Dagham Stone.' Certain bands of the White Limestone yield *Epithyris oxonica* while others are crowded with gastropods such as *Nerinea*, and it was from the base of the White Limestone at Minchinhampton that Morris and Lycett are said to have obtained most of the finely preserved molluscs that are figured in their monograph.

In the North Cotswolds the White Limestone is separated from the freestone division by the Hampen Marly Beds, consisting of 20 to 30 ft. of grey marls and subordinate limestones, frequently crowded with the oyster *Ostrea hebridica*.

Kemble Beds.—At Kemble, near Tetbury, 30 ft. of buff false-bedded oolite, known as the Kemble Beds, rest unconformably upon the White Limestone. They have a wide extension in the Cotswolds, where the unconformable junction with the White Limestone is often well marked by eroded and channelled surfaces. To the east of Cirencester the Kemble Beds become more flaggy; they are then indistinguishable from Forest Marble and have been mapped as that formation as far as the Oxfordshire boundary.

BRADFORD BEDS AND FOREST MARBLE

Bradford Beds.—East of Bath in the Bradford-on-Avon district the Great Oolite Limestone is capped by about 10 ft. of clay—the Bradford Clay, which is overlain in turn by the clays and shelly limestones of the Forest Marble.

The most attractive feature of the Bradford Clay at its type locality is the occasional presence of groups of Pear Encrinites (*Apiocrinus parkinsoni*) attached to the hard floor of Great Oolite limestone underlying the clay, and still in position of growth. It is thought that the presence of so many well-preserved specimens with their stem bases still attached to the limestone floor indicates that they were smothered while still alive by the rapid influx of mud into clear but shallow water.

The brachiopod fauna of the Bradford Clay is rich and distinctive, and includes such forms as *Digonella digona*, *Eudesia cardium*, *Dictyothyris coarctata* and *Epithyris bathonica*. This assemblage has a fairly restricted vertical range over a wide area, and can therefore be used for correlation in the absence of ammonites.

The Bradford Clay fauna has been observed in the Bath—Frome district and in several localities in the Cotswolds as far north as Cirencester. Over the Bath Axis in the Sodbury area, however, the fauna is found in the top 45 ft. of the Great Oolite Limestone and to this limestone facies of the Bradford Beds the name 'Acton Turville Beds' has been applied.

South of the Mendips as far as Wincanton the Bradford Clay fauna has not yet been found, but between this point and the Dorset Coast a thin bed of pale marl known as the Boueti Bed forms the dividing line between the Upper Fuller's Earth Clay and the Forest Marble. The fossils of the Boueti Bed include *Goniorhynchia boueti*, and ossicles of *Apiocrinus*, and it is thought that this bed is the equivalent of a part of the Bradford Beds. The fossils of the Boueti Bed are usually covered with *Serpula*, and the marl composing it sometimes contains pellets of clay possibly derived from the Fuller's Earth clays below. It marks a period when there was a pause in sedimentation probably accompanied by some erosion of the underlying clays.

Forest Marble (Wychwood Beds) and Hinton Sands.—Succeeding the Bradford Beds in North Somerset and Gloucestershire and the Boueti Bed in Mid and South Somerset, there is a series of shelly, false-bedded limestones and clays which constitute the Forest Marble—a name derived from the ancient Forest of Wychwood, in Oxfordshire, where the beds were once extensively worked.

In the Cotswolds area the 'Forest Marble' is shown on the Survey maps as succeeding the Great Oolite, and it has already been stated that in the area between Cirencester and the Oxfordshire boundary, owing to their lithological similarity, the uppermost beds of the Great Oolite—the Kemble Beds—have been mapped as Forest Marble. In this region true Forest Marble, which overlies Bradford Clay, is very thin, whilst the Great Oolite Kemble Beds become thick and assume a 'Forest Marble' facies.

In Somerset the Forest Marble consists of a clay series with a middle division of blue, shelly, conspicuously false-bedded limestones, largely made up of oyster fragments. These limestones form one of the most prominent of the Jurassic escarpments in south-east Somerset.

Starting in the south of the area the Forest Marble outcrop forms the ridge of Birts Hill and runs to Sutton Bingham and Hardington. From here it extends north-east past Sherborne, where it is 130 ft. thick, to Wincanton. At Bowden the limestone was extensively quarried as 'Bowden Marble.' From Wincanton to Frome the beds maintain an approximate thickness of 130 ft. and give rise to the high ground upon which Frome is built.

Northwards between Frome and Freshford the Forest Marble spreads over a considerable tract of country but is somewhat thinner. In the Cotswolds the beds have a wide outcrop though their thickness seldom exceeds 15ft., whilst towards the Oxfordshire boundary there is a further diminution to 8 ft.

Between Cirencester and Fairford the Forest Marble locally furnishes tilestones which are known as 'Poulton Slates.'

Hinton Sands.—This name was applied by William Smith to the sandy facies of the Forest Marble. Locally the sands replace the limestones and clays of the upper part of the Forest Marble and are found at intervals along the outcrop from South Somerset to Cirencester. At the type locality of Hinton Charterhouse, near Bath, they consist of about 30 ft. of white and buff sands with clay pellets and doggers of calcareous sandstone.

XIV. CORNBRASH

OVERLYING THE FOREST MARBLE is the comparatively thin but highly distinctive limestone and marl formation known as the Cornbrash, a term originally applied in Wiltshire to certain stony or brashy soils that are well suited to the growth of cereals. As it frequently overlies a clay formation the Cornbrash is often water-bearing, and its outcrop is usually marked by a line of villages.

The researches of J. A. Douglas and W. J. Arkell have shown that the Cornbrash is divisible into lower and upper parts, corresponding with the two ammonite zones of *Clydoniceras discus* and *Macrocephalites macrocephalus* respectively. Four brachopod faunas can also be recognized, the divisions being as follows:

	Ammonite Zones	*Brachiopod Faunas*
UPPER CORNBRASH	Macrocephalus	*Microthyridina lagenalis* *Microthyridina siddingtonensis*
LOWER CORNBRASH	Discus	*Obovothyris obovata* *Cererithyris intermedia*

According to Douglas and Arkell the Intermedia Beds are almost invariably present where the junction of the Cornbrash and Forest Marble is seen. The Obovata Beds are probably the most widespread and fossiliferous deposit of the Lower Cornbrash and at the same time show the greatest lithological variation. At some localities *Astarte hilpertonensis, Trigonia rolandi* and other lamellibranchs may occur in such profusion in the upper part of the Obovata Beds as to form a veritable *Astarte-Trigonia* Bed.

The Upper Cornbrash is best developed in the Fairford district, but in other places intraformational erosion has led to the development of non-sequences, so that one or more of the brachiopod faunas may be missing.

Where the Cornbrash outcrop is first seen between Southrop and Fairford the Upper Cornbrash largely consists of rather unfossiliferous hard grey flags with thin fossiliferous marl bands. The Lower Cornbrash of this region is usually represented by thin, flaggy limestone.

South-west of Fairford the outcrop of the Cornbrash lies outside our district, which it does not traverse again until the neighbourhood of Malmesbury is reached. Here a striking difference is seen: the Upper Cornbrash is represented by only a thin seam of brown marl containing the zonal ammonite and brachiopods, whilst the Lower Cornbrash consists largely of massive, unfossiliferous, blue-centred limestones known as the 'Corston Beds.' At Corston, near Malmesbury, from which the beds derive their name, these limestones reach an estimated thickness of nearly 50 ft. and have been extensively quarried.

A similar succession of thin Upper Cornbrash resting on more massive Lower Cornbrash rocks extends southwards some 24 miles to the Frome District, but in Somerset the beds show considerable variation. Where the Cornbrash outcrop finally passes out of the region at Stalbridge the Upper Cornbrash has expanded to some 8 ft. of sandy limestone and rests upon the same thickness of Lower Cornbrash.

XV. KELLAWAYS BEDS AND OXFORD CLAY

ALTHOUGH THE OXFORD CLAY attains an average thickness of 500 ft., it is seldom exposed and little is seen of it within the region. It gives rise to heavy clay land with an undulating surface channelled by small streams. At the base of the Oxford Clay Series there is a succession of sands and calcareous sandstones known as the ' Kellaways Beds ', from the hamlet of Kellaways in Wiltshire where the beds are best developed. Traces of Kellaways Beds are to be seen near Cirencester at the South Cerney railway cutting, where huge ' doggers ' occur in loose sands. Between here and Lechlade these beds form a well-marked bank.

In Somerset evidence of the presence of Kellaways Beds was obtained at Witham Friary and Marston Bigot; in the new railway cuttings at Frome, sandy Kellaways Clays were formerly seen overlying the Cornbrash.

XVI. CRETACEOUS

CRETACEOUS ROCKS have a very limited outcrop within the district. To the south-east of Frome high escarpments extending from Longleat to Stourton Tower and the high ground in the neighbourhood of Chard and Crewkerne are formed by Cretaceous strata. The deposits are described in the British Regional Geology handbooks on ' South-West England ' and ' The Hampshire Basin '.

XVII. PLEISTOCENE AND RECENT

THE QUATERNARY PERIOD extends from the end of Pliocene times up to the present day and is usually subdivided into (1) Pleistocene; (2) Holocene or Recent; the line of division between the two groups being drawn at the end of the Great Ice Age.

The formations of the Quaternary Period comprise an extremely varied series of unconsolidated beds which are known as ' Drifts ' or ' Superficial Deposits ' in contrast with earlier formed ' Solid ' formations over which they are spread. Drifts include glacial and fluviatile deposits together with a very mixed group known as ' Head '. The latter, which includes the taele-gravels and other solifluxion products, was formed by snow-sludging and melt waters under periglacial conditions.

Correlation of Pleistocene and Recent deposits is a problem of immense difficulty, since fossil evidence, apart from some vertebrate remains and human artefacts, is extremely rare. A recent great advance has been made in correlation of the alluvial peats by means of pollen analysis. In our present district the relations of the drifts of the Lower Severn Valley have been established by

Professor L. J. Wills and Dr. M. E. Tomlinson, while preliminary investigations upon the peats of the Somerset Levels have been made by Dr. H. Godwin. Professor L. S. Palmer also has made a survey of the Pleistocene deposits of the Bristol district. These results are set out in the accompanying table, to which are added suggested correlatives from South Monmouth and the Bristol Avon valley.

General sequence	Severn Valley		Bristol Avon and Monmouth	Raised Beach, Cave deposits, etc.
	Terrace Gravels	Taele Gravels	Terrace Gravels	
Down-cutting of Deep Channel	?Stroud Terrace			?10-Foot Beach of Woodspring
Magdalenian Little Welsh Glaciation	Worcester Terrace	Reindeer Bed of Uphill		Mendip and Wye Valley Cave Deposits
Aurignacian Interglacial Mousterian Irish Sea Glaciation	Main and Cainscross terraces	Oolite Gravels of Severn Valley	?50-Foot Terrace of Saltford	?50-Foot Beach of Clevedon
Mid Acheulian Great Inter-glacial period	Kidderminster and Whitminster terraces		?100-Foot Terrace at Twerton ?Caerwent Terrace	Burtle Beds
Main Eastern Glaciation ?Inter-glacial	Bushley Green Terrace	Whitminster and high level taele gravel Moreton Drift and Paxford Gravels	?100-Foot Terrace at Shirehampton; Parkwell Terrace	
Great Welsh Glaciation	Wooldridge Terrace	Campden Tunnel Drift		

At the beginning of Pleistocene times the climate became increasingly colder until the greater part of Britain lay beneath ice-caps. The Great Ice Age was not a single prolonged glaciation but a succession of glacial periods separated by milder interglacial periods. In three of the periods the ice approached our district from different quarters, and in so doing carried fragments of the ground over which it had passed; thus the different deposits frequently contain their own characteristic 'indicator rocks'.

Although only in the first two glacial periods did the ice-front actually penetrate our district, the presence of large ice sheets in the vicinity, during succeeding cold periods, had a profound effect upon the climate in the periglacial areas. Here local snow-caps were developed, and during the short seasonal thaws torrents of melt-water carried away rock debris and frozen mud which were deposited in great fans or spreads of taele gravel. Most of the present-day dry valleys were probably formed under such conditions: the frozen subsoil

(A 6293)

THE SOUTH FACE OF THE MENDIPS SEEN ACROSS THE ALLUVIAL FLATS

(A 6291)

THE SOMERSET LEVELS. A VIEW FROM NEAR WEDMORE ACROSS BURTLE HEATH TO THE POLDEN HILLS

did not allow the normal underground percolation of surface water which, as a result, flowed overground and in so doing excavated the valleys.

Melt waters from the large ice-fronts fed the ancestors of the present-day rivers and carried down masses of glacial drift, redepositing the material as terraced river gravels. The valley floor upon which each set of gravels was laid down was graded to sea-level: this varied from time to time so that the ancient sea-beaches are found to-day at widely differing levels.

During the interglacial periods the limestone caves were frequently inhabited by Palaeolithic man, whose remains, together with flint implements and the bones of contemporary wild animals, have been found in the floors of many caves such as those of Cheddar, Burrington Combe and the Wye Valley.

SUMMARY OF EVENTS IN THE LOWER SEVERN VALLEY

At the beginning of Glacial times the sea stood at a very much higher level than it does to-day. The Severn was a moderate-sized river with its headwaters near Ironbridge in Shropshire, and its main tributary was the ancestor of the Warwick Avon. The whole of the Lower Severn drainage system in these early days probably stood at nearly 200 ft. above present-day sea-level.

From the time of the first Great Welsh Glaciation, when a lobe of the ice-front extended down the Severn as far as Gloucester and another lobe pushed over the Moreton gap into the Evenlode Valley the whole history of the river has been one of prolonged downcutting adjusted to a falling sea-level. Periodically this fall was checked and aggradation or terrace building took place on the valley floor.

During the great Mid Acheulian Interglacial Period which followed the melting of the Welsh and Main Eastern ice the Severn deepened its valley and greatly widened the flood plain, and in so doing removed most of the earlier-formed terraces. The succeeding Irish Sea Glaciation dammed up the upper waters of a large river, that had hitherto flowed north-westwards to Cheshire, and forced it into the headwaters of the Severn. The gorge at Ironbridge thus came into being and the diverted drainage has followed this course to the present day. Although the Irish Sea ice did not invade the area, the climate became extremely severe, and it was during this period that the main spreads of taele gravel, composed of local oolitic rocks, were formed on the wide flood plain between the Severn and the Cotswold scarp. In Somerset the fans of taele gravel in the Vale of Ilchester may have originated at this period.

The final Little Welsh Glaciation produced scarcely more than a cold period in the general amelioration of climate.

Following the building up of the Worcester Terrace during this cold period there was a fall in the level of the sea to at least 100 ft. below Ordnance Datum. The Severn cut a deep canyon, extending upstream as far as Gloucester, in the floor of its flat-bottomed valley and most of the Bristol Channel became dry land.

There was soon a quick reversal of events and the sea rose rapidly. The alluvial muds of the river buried the deep channel and wide valley on its flanks and so covered up many of the earlier-formed river terraces.

This post-Glacial transgression which occurred in what is known as the Boreal and Atlantic Periods, took place in stages, the halts being marked by the establishment of beds of peat. From Godwin's preliminary work in Somerset it has been shown that the maximum transgression had already occurred by Neolithic times (2500-2200 B.C.). The climate of Boreal times was mainly warm and dry but during the succeeding Atlantic Period moister conditions set in and the alder-oak-lime type of vegetation became established. The main peat bands of Somerset were formed during this period. In the peat moors remains of Neolithic man have been found in this peat. The sequence of events is diagrammatically shown in Fig. 24.

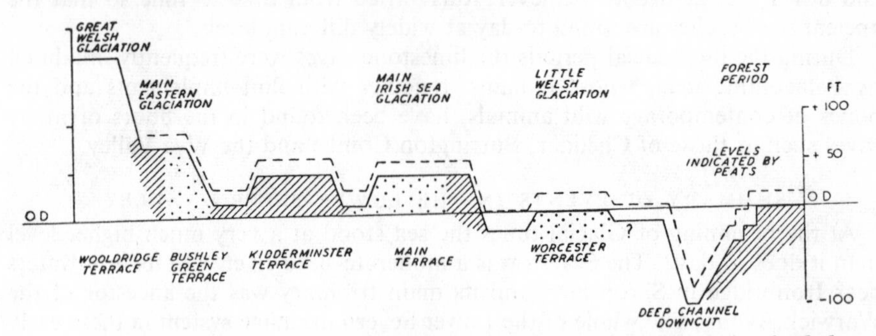

FIG. 24. *Graph to show mean sea-levels and corresponding beach levels deduced from gradient diagrams of the Severn terraces* (After L. J. Wills)

Warm periods shaded; cold periods stippled; mean sea-levels solid lines; beach levels broken lines.

GLACIAL DEPOSITS

Boulder clay and associated glacial gravels, the Moreton Drift, occur in the Vale of Moreton and extend along the Evenlode Valley. The boulder clay is a plastic red-purple clay containing scattered Bunter quartzite pebbles and chalk flints and is evidently a product of the Main Eastern Glaciation. Traces of boulder clay also occur in fissures in the limestone of the North Cotswolds. At the northern end of the Cotswolds, in the gap between Ebrington Hill and Dovers Hill, the Campden Tunnel Drift consists of well-bedded sand and gravel with Bunter pebbles and Welsh igneous rocks. It represents the fluvio-glacial gravel associated with the earlier Great Welsh Glaciation. The Paxford Gravels, composed mainly of local Jurassic limestones, appear to have been formed during the intervening interglacial period.

TERRACE GRAVELS

Although the gravels of the high-level Wooldridge Terrace may be rather fluvio-glacial in character, the remainder of the Severn Terraces are definitely stratified sands and gravels laid down by river action. The earlier formed terraces always occupy a higher level than the latter; when traced upstream from the present river mouth they are seen to rise gradually in height above O.D. Thus at the Severn Tunnel the top of the Kidderminster Terrace is 51 ft. O.D., whilst at Tewkesbury it lies at 105 ft.

Owing to subsequent dissection, the four chief terraces now occur as small isolated patches of gravel on the western side of the Severn, whilst the Worcester Terrace is only seen between Gloucester and Tewkesbury. Generally speaking the terraces are of sand and gravel, the latter consisting of Bunter quartzite pebbles, flints and rolled fragments of local rocks. The gravel of the older terraces is often extremely coarse in texture. In the coastal region of South Monmouthshire the Caerwent and Parkwall gravels may be tentatively correlated with the Kidderminster and Bushley Green Terraces.

The River Frome (Stroud Water) which joins the Severn near Framilode has formed three terraces which have been correlated with those of the Severn. In this case, however, the gravels consist almost entirely of rolled Jurassic rocks. From the chief of these deposits, the Cainscross Terrace, which is correlated with the Severn Main Terrace, a cold fauna has been obtained: this includes mammoth, woolly rhinoceros and ox.

Terrace gravels also occur at different levels along the Bristol Avon. At Victoria Pit, Twerton is a terrace composed mainly of local Jurassic rocks with a base at about 80 ft. O.D. The lowest part of the gravels has yielded animal remains including *Elephas antiquus*. Near Saltford the 50-ft Terrace, composed of subangular gravel, forms a wide spread at Stidham Farm. At Shirehampton very coarse gravels occur at about 100 ft. O.D. Possible correlation of these terraces with those of the Severn, based on grading of levels, is shown in the accompanying table.

HEAD DEPOSITS

These include the great spreads of taele-gravels and the scree-like unstratified masses of limestone debris. The former include the great fans of oolitic gravel that extend over the Isbourne Valley from Winchcombe to Evesham. A further sheet lies between Bredon Hill and the Carrant Brook. Extensive deposits of oolitic gravels occur around Cheltenham, through Gloucester to beyond the Frome Valley, and are well displayed in the pits around Barnwood, Gloucester, where they have yielded remains of mammoth and woolly rhinoceros. In the neighbourhood of Cheltenham they include thick deposits of quartzose sand and are known as the Cheltenham Sands and Gravels. Locally, as at Charlton Kings, the deposits may reach a thickness of 50 ft.

These oolitic gravels have been correlated with the Main Terrace of the Severn.

In South Somerset the Head Deposits of the Vale of Ilchester consist of poorly stratified oolitic and flinty gravel mixed with Liassic material.

Close to the Cotswold scarp masses of unbedded oolitic limestone gravel probably represent ancient screes, whilst the Pleistocene breccias of the Weston-Clevedon district, composed of angular Carboniferous Limestone in a matrix of loamy sand are probably of the same nature.

ALLUVIUM

The alluvial flats have the greatest surface spread of any of the Quaternary deposits. The Somerset Levels, between the Quantocks and the Mendips, form the second largest fenland in England. Another great area occurs between the Clevedon Ridge and the Mendips, whilst a wide coastal strip extends northwards from Portishead to near Berkeley. In Monmouthshire the Caldicot Levels extend from Portskewet to the mouth of the River Usk.

These deposits consist of blue muds and silty sands and reach a considerable thickness. At Weston-super-Mare 91 ft. were proved and near Huntspill the formation was over 60 ft. thick. Near the top, about the level of Ordnance Datum, two beds of peat are often found in the coastal belt. The uppermost band, containing stumps of alder and yew, may be seen in the brickpit at Combwich, north-west of Bridgwater: it is also seen in the Royal Potteries pit at Weston-super-Mare. Away from this coastal belt are the remains of raised peat bogs, as at Shapwick and Meare heaths, where the peat is up to

16 ft. in thickness. Here peat has been extensively dug, the working probably dating back to Roman times.

RAISED BEACH DEPOSITS

Raised beach deposits do not include one at 100 ft. above the present sea-level, though there is evidence of the existence of a 50-ft. raised beach along the coast from Portishead to Brean Down. South of this the beach runs inland to the foot of the Mendips. At Portishead the beach is indicated by pebbles overlain by blown sand. At Bleadon the old beach platform is covered by a terrestrial breccia with a sandy matrix. These deposits have yielded many mammalian remains, including bones of horse, bear, wolf, fox, etc., as well as species of terrestrial molluscs. At Bleadon and Brean Down the Pleistocene deposits yielded many reindeer antlers, while superficial strata contain the remains of pig, deer, etc. Between the latter relatively recent deposits and those which contain remains of reindeer lie many feet of unstratified terrestrial limestone breccia, or Head. The 10-ft. raised beach is to be seen between Portishead and Clevedon as a wave-cut rock platform bearing masses of old beach pebbles.

Burtle Beds.—In the vicinity of Middlezoy, Somerset, there occurs a series of shelly sands and gravels which are known as the Burtle Beds. The fossils include common and widely distributed marine shells, and more rarely the brackish water *Corbicula fluminalis.* Bones and teeth of elephant, rhinoceros and bison have also been found. The Burtle Beds are considered to represent littoral deposits formed during the subsidence which ended with the formation of the 50-ft. Raised Beach.

CAVE DEPOSITS

Cave deposits in the district have been well investigated. In Pleistocene times the caves were inhabited by lion, bear, hyaena, wolf, fox, etc. The deposits at the Hyaena Den, near Wookey Hole, are of Mid Pleistocene age, while those in the Uphill and Clevedon caves are of Middle to Late Pleistocene age. Aveline's Hole, in Burrington Combe, Gough's Cave in Cheddar Gorge and the caves of the Wye Valley have yielded a number of artefacts and mammalian remains. In the cave earth of Aveline's Hole reindeer, giant deer, red deer, horse, lynx, shorthorn ox, pig, brown bear and wolf have been found, as well as human skeletons and many flint implements—a Late Pleistocene assemblage. In the Wye Valley, King Arthur's Cave has yielded bones of lion, hyaena, cave bear, mammoth, Irish deer and woolly rhinoceros. Remains of man show that the cave had been occupied during Upper Palaeolithic, Mesolithic, Neolithic and later times.

XVIII. ECONOMIC GEOLOGY

COAL, LIMESTONE and Fuller's Earth have already been mentioned as being some of the chief economic products of the district, while peat, sand and gravel are worked locally, but in addition to these, iron, lead, zinc, manganese, celestine, gypsum and barytes are or have been worked.

IRON

The iron ores of the Forest of Dean have been worked since Roman times, the ancient outcrop workings being known as ' scowles.' Most of the mining ceased at the beginning of the present century with the approaching exhaustion of the ore-field.

The main ores are ' brown haematites ' (hydrated ferric oxides) with which are included the crystalline form known as goethite. The metallic iron varies from 15 per cent to 65 per cent. The ore occurs as irregular pockets, lodes and veins partly replacing the Carboniferous Limestone in which the Crease Limestone is the chief repository: ore is also found in the Drybrook Sandstone and Lower Dolomite. The ore-bodies, which decrease in depth, were deposited from descending iron-bearing solutions, the open-jointed limestone being highly susceptible to permeation and metasomatic replacement.

The iron carbonates and pyrites of the Coal Measures shales appear to have been the primary source of the iron: weathering under the desert conditions of Permo-Carboniferous times appears to have given rise to an iron-rich surface from which solutions descended into the underlying rocks.

In the Bristol and Somerset area haematite lodes in the fissured Pennant Sandstone were formerly worked at Iron Acton, Frampton Cotterell and Temple Cloud.

The red and yellow earthy iron oxides known as ' oxide ' and ' ochre ' have been worked at several localities in the region for the manufacture of pigments. Winford and Wick are the chief centres of ochre work at the present time, the material being dug from pockets in the Carboniferous Limestone or from bedded deposits of Triassic age.

LEAD

The Mendip Hills were famous in bygone days for their production of lead and zinc ores, but to-day the mining industry is completely abandoned. The sites of the ' old mineries ' are marked by ruined buildings and heaps of slag as at Priddy, Charterhouse and East Harptree, whilst scarred and furrowed fields, locally termed ' gruffy-grounds,' mark the sites of old ore-workings.

The principal ore of lead, worked in the Mendip Hills, was galena (PbS, lead sulphide), which commonly occurred in veins or lodes in the Carboniferous Limestone, accompanied by calcite and, more rarely, barytes. Lead mining was in progress in Roman times. The industry reached its peak between 1628 and 1659; a rapid decline then set in, probably owing to the exhaustion of ore in the lodes near the surface and to pumping apparatus being inadequate to free the deeper mines of water. Mendip lead was never of the best quality, its main use being in the manufacture of lead-shot. The process of dropping molten lead from a height into water to form lead shot was invented by a Bristol plumber and the original shot-tower at Redcliffe, Bristol, stands to this day.

In the nineteenth century some of the old mineries were reconditioned by Cornish engineers, who re-worked the half-smelted slags or ' slimes ' left by the Romans, and in addition to lead a considerable quantity of silver was recovered.

Lead workings of great antiquity exist at Pen Park Hole, Brentry, where galena associated with calcite and barytes occurs in almost vertical veins following the strike of the Carboniferous Limestone.

ZINC

The chief zinc ore was calamine ($ZnCO_3$, zinc carbonate) which occurred mainly in the Dolomitic Conglomerate, either in the form of irregular veins or as small particles mixed with gritty earth.

The zinc industry had a much shorter existence than that of the lead, for calamine mining did not start until the reign of Elizabeth. During the eighteenth century, when the lead mining was becoming defunct, Mendip miners turned actively to the mining of calamine. The ore was mixed with copper to make brass, calamine-brass works being established at Bristol in 1702. When later it was known that calamine yielded metallic zinc, commercially known as spelter, Mendip calamine was in considerable demand to supply Bristol spelter works. The headquarters of the calamine industry were the villages of Shipham and Rowberrow. Towards the end of the nineteenth century calamine mining became extinct, partly owing to the exhaustion of the ore, partly to the decline of the calamine-brass industry, but mainly owing to the abolition of protective duties against foreign zinc.

MANGANESE

Small quantities of the earthy oxide of manganese, pyrolusite (MnO_2, manganese dioxide) occur in the Dolomitic Conglomerate of the Mendips at East Harptree, at Higher Pitts, near Ebbor, at Croscombe and at Wadbury. Much of the ore was used by potteries for imparting a black colour to the ware, but at Wadbury it was used in the local ironworks to harden steel. It is no longer mined.

BARYTES

Barytes ($BaSO_4$, barium sulphate) is found filling fissures in the Carboniferous Limestone of Cannington Park, near Bridgwater, where it has been worked.

Barytes is used as a substitute for lead in the preparation of white paint, and as a ' filler ' or ' bleach ' for cloths.

CELESTINE

Celestine ($SrSO_4$, strontium sulphate) has been dug for many years in the region between Cromhall, Yate and Stanshawe's Court, where it occurs in irregular masses in the Keuper Marl or in secondary concentrations near the junction between the Keuper Marl and underlying rocks.

Much of the output was formerly exported to Germany for use in the refining of sugar-beet: it is used as a ' filler ' in special paints and for the production of crimson flames in pyrotechnics.

GYPSUM

Gypsum ($CaSO_4$, $2H_2O$, hydrated calcium sulphate) is found in nodular masses forming an impersistent bed in the Keuper Marls, and as secondary strings and veins. From time to time it has been worked on the foreshore at Watchet.

Its main uses are as a substitute for kaolin as a filler in paper surfacing, for plaster making and as a fertiliser.

BRICK, TILE AND POTTERY CLAYS

A large brickmaking industry utilizes the wide variety of brick-clays and marls found within the region.

Household bricks, tiles and pots are made from clays of the Old Red Sandstone, Trias, Lias and Alluvium, whilst the Coal Measures clays are used for the manufacture of engineering bricks and large pipes.

Around Bridgwater the fine silty alluvium of the River Parret is utilized to make ' Bath Bricks,' used for scouring purposes.

WATER SUPPLY

Large supplies of water are derived from springs or underground sources in the region, but in an area of such geological complexity water must necessarily be drawn from a wide variety of formations if the needs of the population cannot be met from surface sources.

Of the water-bearing formations the older Palaeozoic rocks yield only infinitesimal quantities and may be disregarded.

Considerable quantities of water are obtained from the sandstone and conglomerates at the top of the Old Red Sandstone on the eastern side of the Forest of Dean, but in the Bristol and Somerset Coalfield large supplies are not normally present.

The Carboniferous Limestone on the other hand is one of the best source rocks in the region. Large public supplies are derived from perennial springs or underground streams and rivers issuing from the foot of limestone hills. Such ' overflow springs ' are due to the confining of the limestone waters by the impermeable Red Marls banked against the limestone and its marginal fringe of Dolomitic Conglomerate. Most of Bristol's water-supply as well as that of Burnham, Weston-super-Mare and many parts of north-west Somerset comes from this source.

Fissured Pennant Sandstone and other thick grits and sandstones occurring in the Coal Measures also yield much water. Many drowned and abandoned shafts of coal and iron workings have been adapted for this purpose both in the Forest of Dean and the Bristol Coalfield. Current working of the mines, the draining of the country by adits and pumping from old pits has greatly lowered the water table in these areas. This has resulted in the drying-up or excessive lowering of the levels of many of the older wells in the Coal Measures and has led to the development of an extensive network of piped supplies fed by central pumping stations.

In the New Red Sandstone both the Dolomitic Conglomerate (mentioned above) and the Keuper Sandstones are important aquifers.

The Red Marls are waterless, or yield hard and saline waters, but the Keuper sandstones interbedded with the marls yield important supplies in North Somerset, Bristol and North Gloucestershire. The Lias is a bad formation for water-supply, only minor quantities being obtained from the White Lias and Blue Lias limestones, while in the overlying thick clays saline waters such as those of Cheltenham Spa are frequently encountered. In areas such as Central Somerset and the Vale of Gloucester, many small and often unsatisfactory supplies are obtained from patches of head or gravel resting on clay.

Some water supplies are obtained from the Upper Lias sands—as, for example, from the Midford Sands in the Bath district—but on the whole these rocks contain too much silt to yield large constant supplies. In this sense the geological nomenclature is misleading and considerable disappointment has been caused where borings have been made in the sands in the hope of obtaining water.

The overlying Inferior Oolite and Great Oolite limestones are important aquifers and provide supplies for part of south-east Somerset and for much of the otherwise waterless uplands of the Cotswolds.